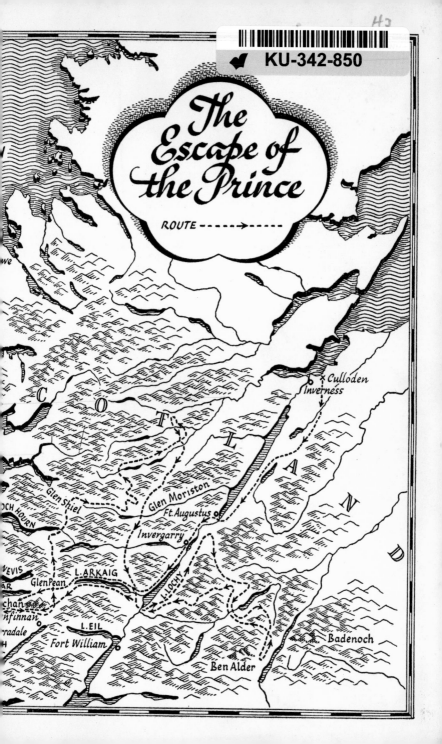

THE ESCAPE OF THE PRINCE

Prince Charles

THE ESCAPE OF
THE PRINCE

by

JANE LANE

with illustrations by

DOUGLAS RELF

LONDON
EVANS BROTHERS LIMITED

By the same author:

THE ESCAPE OF THE KING
THE ESCAPE OF THE QUEEN
THE ESCAPE OF THE DUKE
DESPERATE BATTLE

First published, 1951
Reprinted 1952
Reprinted 1958
Reprinted 1961

Printed in Great Britain for Evans Brothers Limited
Montague House, Russell Square, London, W.C.1, by
Richard Clay and Company, Ltd., Bungay, Suffolk
z5556   PR5646

To

The boys and girls of the Highlands,
whose forefathers took part in this true story.

CONTENTS

ILLUSTRATIONS

1

The Fugitive Prince

THE dawn of a bitter cold April day was breaking over the Scottish Highlands, when the sound of urgent hoof-beats disturbed the silence of the moors.

They came at a hard gallop, scattering the flints on the lonely road; the horses were drenched with sweat and lather, and often stumbled, for they were quite spent with fatigue. Through the little clachan or village they galloped, and so up to the big house called Invergarry, where the riders drew rein. No one came to greet the travellers or to enquire their business here, for Invergarry stood empty and deserted, with no smoke coming from its chimneys, no hangings at the windows, no dogs barking an alarm. For a few minutes the eight horse-men sat slumped in their saddles, the breath gasping in their throats; their clothes were torn and stained, their faces blackened with gun-smoke and haggard with exhaustion, and some of them were covered in blood.

After a while, one of the company, a very tall young man in a fine laced coat with the blue ribbon of the Order of the Garter crossing it, and with a white periwig which

9

now hung uncurled upon his neck, raised his head and after staring dazedly about him, enquired in a hoarse voice where they were.

"It is Invergarry we are at, your Royal Highness," answered Ned Burke, one of his companions. Ned spoke English haltingly, for he had never spoken anything but Gaelic, the language of the Highlands, until he was thirty years old. " It is the house of MacDonald of Glengarry, but this Chief will not be at home just now, and I'm thinking his house will not be furnished."

" We could ask for food and shelter in the village yonder," said another of the company.

" The people of the clachan will have taken to the hills when they were after hearing of the battle," replied Ned, shaking his head.

" We must make so bold as to force an entrance into Invergarry," said the tall young man whom Ned had addressed as ' your Royal Highness' , " and apologise for our discourtesy to its owner afterwards. For rest we must have, we and our horses, or there will be an end of us all."

So they broke the lock of the door and entered. It was almost as cold indoors as without, but at least they were sheltered from the wind and the cold, stinging sleet. The house was more like a castle than a mansion, and its being unfurnished made it seem very melancholy. Their footsteps echoed through the empty rooms, and the sleet spat viciously upon the windows. While some of his companions took the horses to the stables and tried to find water and hay for them, the tall young man flung himself down on the floor of one of the bedrooms, just as he was, and tried to sleep.

His name was Charles Edward Stuart, but those who loved him spoke of him as Bonnie Prince Charlie. He was twenty-five years old, and ever since he was born he had lived in exile, chiefly in France, for his grandfather, King James the Second of England and Seventh of Scotland, had been driven from his throne by disloyal nobles, and his father, the rightful King James the Third and Eighth, had never been able to recover his inheritance. But young Charles Edward, from the age when he had been able to understand about it all, had been determined to come over to Britain and win back the throne for his father.

In order to fit himself for his great adventure, he had spent his boyhood in learning the art of war, and in hardening his body by manly exercises. Last year he had come to Scotland, with only seven companions and no money or arms, and he had appealed to the people of the Highlands, the chiefs and their clansmen, to fight for him against the German usurper who had got his father's throne. They were a very loyal people, and so they had risen for him, and he and they had fought so bravely that they had cut their way to within ninety miles of London. But German George, the usurper, had great wealth and a large, well-paid army on his side, and so he had forced Charles and his Highlanders to retreat; and yesterday his son, the Duke of Cumberland, had defeated Charles utterly at a place called Culloden near Inverness, with ten thousand trained soldiers against Charles's five thousand half-starved, untrained Highlanders. So the Prince was a fugitive, his brave men scattered, captured, or dead, and unless Charles could escape back to France, he also would be captured and put to death.

He had ridden forty miles last night; for five days and nights before that he had had no proper food or sleep, and what with this, and the misery of his defeat, he was quite spent. As he lay here on the hard floor at Invergarry, it seemed to him impossible that he would ever get out of Scotland alive. The enemy troops were everywhere, occupying forts and strong places throughout the Highlands, and now they would all be concentrating on his capture. He had been guided to Invergarry by good, honest Ned Burke, who was a sedan-chairman in Edinburgh, but had served as a volunteer in the Prince's army, and had been born and reared in the Highlands. Ned had told him that his one chance of escape was to make towards the west coast, where if he was lucky he might find a ship to take him over to France. Charles thought this most unlikely, because all the ports would be guarded, and in any case he did not see how he was to avoid being captured on the way. But as no one else had had any suggestions to make, he had let Ned guide him to Invergarry, where, after some rest, they must plan what next to do.

Charles fell asleep at last from sheer exhaustion, and he was still asleep when, about two o'clock in the afternoon, Ned came on tiptoe into the room where he was. Ned stood looking down on him for a few minutes, and though he was a plain, rough man of nearly forty, he could not help the tears coming into his eyes as he looked at the sprawling figure on the floor. For like all the men who had fought with the Prince, Ned loved and admired him; Charles was so young and handsome, so brave and cheerful and kind, so merciful in victory and so courageous in defeat, and here he was now, a hunted fugitive, his clothes torn and dirty, his fair hair, from which the periwig had fallen, plastered to his head with sweat, and his tired young body resting on a bare and dusty floor. Presently he groaned a little, stirred, and sat up, blinking his large, bright hazel eyes at Ned, and wondering for a moment where on earth he was.

"I was after catching some salmon in the loch," explained Ned, trying to sound cheerful, " and though it is cooked but ill, I not having any butter to dress it, the thought was on me that your Royal Highness would not despise it for your little-meal."

Charles smiled at him, and said how kind and clever it was of Ned to have caught the salmon. But he would not eat until he had heard that his fellow fugitives had had their share. Then he took the fish, which Ned had laid up in two large leaves, and began to eat it with his fingers, sitting there on the floor, and he made Ned eat some of it with him.

"What do you mean by the little-meal, Ned?" he

asked, as they ate. " This seems a great meal to me, and indeed I have never tasted anything more delicious."

" We have but two meals in the Highlands," explained Ned, " the little one at the beginning of the day, and the great one at the end of it. But my sorrow! I am not knowing where your Royal Highness will find your great-meal this evening."

" We shall find it, if God please," replied Charles, " for He has a way of caring for hunted men. I was thinking ere I slept," he went on, " that we are too large a party to travel with any safety on this flight, and therefore I shall take farewell presently of all the company save Captain O'Sullivan, Captain O'Neil, and yourself. These two being Irish gentlemen, and not knowing the Highlands, could not conceal themselves as the others can, and you I will take with me as my guide, and as my cook likewise, for you have shown yourself a bonny one at cooking, Ned."

" I will go with your Royal Highness whithersoever you permit me," said Ned. " But the thought is on me that you should change clothes with me before we continue our journey, for there will be sure to be a description of your Royal Highness published to all the red soldiers who are seeking you, and therefore you ought to disguise yourself as best you can."

Charles agreed to this sensible suggestion, and put on Ned's rough clothes. His own white periwig he hid in a cupboard, and he drew the flat blue Highland bonnet Ned had been wearing well down on his head, in order to conceal his famous fair hair. Then they went downstairs, and after a sorrowful parting from those who were not coming any further with him, Charles set out on horseback with Ned and the two captains, following the road to the west.

Captain O'Sullivan was a fat, jolly gentleman, very fond of comfort and quite unaccustomed to hardship. Captain O'Neil was a young man, but very apt to be gloomy and cast down and to see the dark side of things; so that these two were not the most cheerful companions to have in such a situation. O'Neil kept saying he was sure they would never succeed in gaining the coast, that at any moment they would be surprised by the soldiers, and that really they might just as well give themselves up and have done with it; while his fellow captain moaned continually about the badness of the road, about having to ride in wet clothes which would certainly give him a chill, and about not having had any proper breakfast. Charles was just as anxious as they were about their plight, and very depressed because of his defeat and what it would mean to the loyal men who had fought for him, but he made no complaint himself, but sang some songs to try to cheer them all up.

They rode for thirty miles along the north side of Loch Arkaig, sometimes narrowly avoiding treacherous bogs, at others having to ford through streams or to push their way through dead bracken which came up to the horses' withers and concealed holes and large stones. The horses were not used to such going, as were the little stout native shelties, as they called the Highland ponies, and it was really a wonder that they kept their feet. Sleet and rain fell all that day, soaking and half blinding them, and the wind blew down on them with icy breath from the hills. It was strange to hear the cuckoo calling, for it was more like the depth of winter than mid-April; snow covered the mountains and ice cracked beneath the horses' hooves.

At last, when night had fallen, they saw ahead of them some little twinkling lights. They dared not approach the clachan, though they desperately needed food and shelter, but Ned said he would go forward on foot and find out where they were. He returned presently to say that they were come to Glenpean, and that he had met with one, Donald Cameron, a very honest man and loyal to the Prince, who had said that for one night at least he could entertain them in his house. But they must dismount and stable their horses in an old, disused hut away from the clachan, because otherwise all the people would know that they were fugitives from the battle. Donald Cameron would come to the hut later and attend to the horses.

So, guided by Ned Burke, they made their way into the little village. Donald Cameron's house was the largest it contained, yet it was only like a small cottage. Like all Highland houses, it was round; it had no chimney, but only a hole in the roof for the smoke, and it was thatched with reeds, over which were laid heather ropes weighted with large stones to prevent the roof being swept away in a gale. There was a peat-stack on one side of it and a cow-byre on the other, and indoors the rooms were divided from one another by wicker partitions instead of walls. Because of the wind, the smoke from the peat fire was blown back into the living-room and made the Prince cough because he was not used to it; there were upturned butter-kegs for seats, a kist or chest full of oatmeal, a brine-tub containing the pickled beef on which these people lived all winter, and some hens roosting on the rafters, from which hung strings of onions and puddings of oatmeal and suet.

Charles was so tired when he came to Donald Cameron's home, that he scarcely noticed what his host was like, except that he was very deaf, and had an odd habit of scratching his nose. He had sent his wife and children off to bed, and himself served the fugitives with a meal. Afterwards he showed them into a room where there were some beds of heather, and on these they lay down without undressing. Charles was still drunk with sleep when he was roused next morning before it was light, given a breakfast of bannocks and butter, with a drink of ewe's milk, and told that he must be on his way again. He tried to make Donald Cameron accept some payment for his hospitality, but this was a mistake, because Donald, though he was very poor, like all High-landers was very proud, and he was almost affronted by being offered money for something he considered his duty.

After some hours' travelling, they came to a part of the country where it was quite impossible to proceed on horseback, because there were no roads at all. So they were obliged to dismount, and, after leaving their horses with a friendly man who promised to look after them, they must now proceed on foot. O'Sullivan grumbled terribly at this, and they had not gone half a mile before he was puffing and panting and saying how tired he was. Charles laughed at him, and said that he ought to have hunted and shot with him in France, and so have hardened his body to bear discomfort and fatigue.

They walked all the rest of the day, and right through the following night, making their way across the Braes of Morar towards the coast. Their progress was slow, partly because they had to suit their pace to that of O'Sullivan, who crawled along like a snail, and partly because no one could walk really fast over such country, especially in the darkness. When morning dawned again, they could go no further, but laid themselves down in the heather, seeking some rest before deciding what to do next. But Charles was too anxious to sleep, and leaving his companions he went into a little wood of birches and firs, from which he could see the surrounding country. To his joy he discovered that their long march had brought them within sight of the coast; below him was a sea-loch, and he thought that if he could find a boat, he might sail round to one of the ports and perhaps get a ship to take him to France.

While he was thinking this, suddenly he saw the figure of a man coming towards him up the hill.

His first impulse was to hide, but then he reflected

that if the man had seen him it would look very suspicious, and also, as the figure was plainly that of a Highlander, Charles was sure he could trust him, at least sufficiently to enquire about a boat. So he remained boldly where he was, and watched the man approaching nearer and nearer. He was a very tall old man, dressed in the Highland fashion; he wore a coarse, saffron-coloured shirt, smeared with grease for warmth, and over it the plaid, which was like a great tartan blanket, belted at the waist to form a sort of skirt or kilt to his knees, and gathered round the upper part of his body like a shawl. His bare feet were thrust into deer-skin brogues, with the red hair worn on the outside; over his thick black hair, which was plentifully intermixed with grey, he wore a flat blue bonnet with a sprig of juniper fastened in it. He was a little stooped with age, yet he walked strongly, helped by a long thick stick which, as Charles knew, was called a cromach and was made very cunningly from a hazel root.

When the old man saw Charles he paused for a moment, shading his keen black eyes against the light. Then he gave vent to a low, startled exclamation in the Gaelic, and hurried towards the lonely figure of the Prince which stood in the shadow of the trees. When he came level with it, he made a courteous little bow, removed his bonnet, and, to Charles's surprise, addressed him in English. Like all Highlanders when speaking in this unfamiliar tongue, he made his Ds sound like Ts, and drew out his Ss in a kind of hiss.

19

"The blessing of the Trinity be upon your Royal Highness," said the old man. "I have been at seeking you these two days."

"You know me, it seems," said Charles wonderingly, "but I do not know you."

"By your leave," said the old man, "my name is Donald MacLeod, and I am from Guatergill in the island of Skye. When news of the great battle at Culloden was reaching me, I set out at once to seek your Royal Highness, that I might be at conveying you to the Isles, where you will be safer than you can be upon the continent."

Charles could not at first make out what he meant by the ' continent ', but then he remembered that he had heard other Highlanders refer to the mainland by this term. He asked curiously :

"But how did you know me, Donald ? For you cannot have looked to find me in this wild spot, and besides I am in disguise."

The old man's lips parted in a smile.

"Ach," said he, "it is not a very good disguise whatever. We must be at changing it for a better one presently, but just now I am after thanking the Great Being " (he lifted his eyes reverently to heaven) " that I have found you safe."

"Donald," said Charles earnestly, "you see I am in distress. I therefore throw myself into your bosom, and let you do with me what you will. I am sure you are an honest man and fit to be trusted."

"My grief ! " cried Donald, very much moved, " but

what can I be doing for your Royal Highness? For I am an old, poor man, and can do little for myself."

"You could get me a boat and take me to the Isles as you suggested, Donald," said the Prince. "That is to say, if you are acquainted with these waters, which I hear are very dangerous to the mariner."

"There is not," said Donald proudly, "one mile of coast, nor is there one strip of water in these parts which I am not knowing as I know my own croft at home, for it is my business very often to come to the continent and buy meal for my people in Skye."

"Then will you help me, Donald MacLeod?" asked Charles, impulsively holding out his hands to him.

The old man took them, and held them tightly for a moment in his own gnarled ones.

"May I never," said he deeply, "earn the fame of the song, as my people say, if I desert my Prince in his need. I will be after going directly to hire a boat, and while I am gone, do your Royal Highness and those with you bide close in the heather till I return, that I may know where to be at finding you when I have got the boat."

"We will lie as quiet as the roe-deer when they hear the feet of the hunter," promised Charles, smiling at him.

The old man lifted one of the Prince's slim hands to his lips, twinkled approvingly at him, and said simply:

"That's you!"

2

The Terrible Storm

It was nearly five days before Donald MacLeod returned, and during all that time Charles and his three companions skulked in the heather, one of them always acting as sentry in case the soldiers appeared.

They had nothing to eat except some oatmeal which Donald Cameron had given them before they left his house, but Ned Burke managed to catch some trout in a burn. He caught them with his bare hands by the method known as 'guddling'; Charles was eager to learn the trick, and spent many hours practising it, for he was sure it would come in useful during his flight. The weather continued cold and rainy, and being without any shelter except what they could find under a large rock, they were very uncomfortable. O'Sullivan and O'Neil grumbled worse than ever and were most depressing companions; they kept assuring the Prince that Donald MacLeod would never keep faith with him, and that really they had better try to find a boat for themselves. Charles was very low in spirits himself, partly because he was not at all well, for being continually wet through had brought on a kind of dysentery. But he knew that the most cowardly thing a man can do is to despair, and that the best sort of courage is that of holding on when everything seems at its blackest. So he said to the two captains :

"Is this all the faith and trust you have in the Almighty ? Let us only take care to have enough of faith and trust in His providence and there is no fear for us at all. Pull up your spirits, friends. Never despair."

His own faith was justified when, on April 26th, just ten days after that dreadful Battle of Culloden and five since Donald had left them, they heard from over the hill a human voice imitating the song of the willow-warbler, which has a very distinctive cry, a few high notes falling into a lower key, this being the prearranged signal that Donald had returned to them. Donald was very cheerful; he had hired an eight-oared boat, he said, and a party of rowers he could trust with the Prince's secret; she was lying in Lochnannagh, a mile away, and they could put off that very night. He proposed making for Scalpa, a little island where there lived a very good friend of his, who would entertain Charles and his companions until they could hear of a ship to take them to France.

While they were waiting for the twilight to come, and were eating some food which Donald had brought them, the old man gave them the news, which was very bad indeed. So far as he could understand, almost all the chiefs who had fought for the Prince at Culloden had been captured or killed; among the latter was Lochiel, the Chief of Clan Cameron, and one of the most loyal and noble gentlemen in the Highlands. When Charles heard this, he had to go away by himself for a little while so as not to distress the others with his grief, for he had loved Lochiel more than any of the other chiefs who had fought for him.

Then, said Donald, the Duke of Cumberland had done such dreadful things to the wounded and the prisoners after the battle, burning some of them alive, shooting others in cold blood, and even murdering women and children, that people were calling him the Butcher. He was certain, it seemed, that the Prince had escaped from the battlefield, and he had sent dispatches to that effect to his father, German George, in London, who straight-way had offered the reward of thirty thousand pounds to anyone who could capture the Prince, dead or alive. Cumberland was sure that the Highlanders, being so poor, would be eager to earn so huge a sum of money. Lastly, Donald told Charles that not only were all the red-coat troops in Scotland concentrated on searching for him, but that the Militia had been given the same task. Now the Militia was composed of those few clans who were disloyal to Charles and his father; their fellow-Highlanders called them the Black Watch, because they wore a dark tartan; and because these men knew the country much better than did the red soldiers, and were expert at climbing mountains, they could find Charles much more easily than the regular troops could do.

All this was very depressing news; and as so often happens in life, when one thing goes wrong, nothing else seemed to go right. Just as Charles and the others were about to go down to the shore of the loch where the boat was waiting for them, old Donald stopped, listened, and began to snuff the air like a stag. Then he shook his wise old head, muttered something in the Gaelic, and told the Prince that he feared they would not be able to set out that night after all, because a great storm was coming. Charles asked him how he knew this, for though it was blowing a little and the night was dark, the rain had ceased, and as it was two nights after the full moon, it was quite natural that it should be dark until about half past eleven.

" Are you not after hearing," said Donald, " the seals whining and barking on the rocks down-by ? That is a sure sign of storm, and moreover I can smell it. By your leave, it will be a terrible tempest whatever."

" I would face a storm rather than stay skulking in the heather any longer," said Charles. " And you yourself were saying that I am in much greater danger on the mainland—the continent—than I shall be if I can get to the Isles."

Donald shook his head, but reluctantly agreed to set off, and so they went down to the little creek on the lochside where they found the boat hauled up on the shore. It was too dark to see her properly, but Charles could tell that she was a stout boat, and as he had always loved the sea, he was not at all afraid of the coming voyage. Donald presented the seven rowers to him; they had been told by Donald who he really was, but in case anyone should be lurking about they used no ceremony towards him when they were presented, merely doffing their bonnets and shaking hands with him in the usual polite fashion of their race. One of them was Donald's own son, Murdoch, a lad of fifteen. Murdoch was at the Grammar School at Inverness, but when he had heard that the Prince's army was in the neighbourhood, he had got himself a claymore or Highland sword, a pistol and a dirk, had run away from his lesson-books and fought at Culloden like a man.

They pushed off from the shore into the dark, dangerous waters. All Highland lochs are dangerous, full of currents and submerged rocks, and troubled very suddenly by storms. In daytime the water was so clear that you could see the sand and weeds many feet below, but now it was black as ink and frightening. Donald took the helm, asking Charles to sit down between his knees, O'Sullivan and O'Neil crouched uncomfortably in the stern, and the seven rowers, with Ned Burke, thrust the oars into the pins. At first they rowed in silence, hearing only the squeak of the oars in the rowlocks, the cloop-cloop of water round the sides, the barking of the seals on the rocks, and the voice of the night wind. But presently the wind seemed to be drowning every other sound, and then Charles knew that Donald had been right, and that a great storm was coming.

26

It came racing up from the west, a gale blowing dead in their faces, and bringing with it drenching rain. It whipped the loch into a fury of waves, so that the boat was riding high one moment, sinking deep, deep into troughs the next, till Charles thought they must be diving into the fathomless depths. He remembered then some horrible stories he had heard about Highland lochs, of how a man drowned in them was never seen again, of enormous eels which lived on underwater ledges and swallowed a man at a gulp, and of ships and boats which never returned to harbour. Soon a sound like distant cannon-fire grumbled in the west, and then the sky ahead of them was riven by a forked tongue of light, so that for an instant they could see each other's faces clearly, though the night was black as pitch. Three minutes later, the thunder and the lightning were right over their heads, crashing and flickering in a most terrifying manner. It reminded Charles of that awful Battle of Culloden, when the enemy's artillery had mown down the ranks of his Highlanders like corn.

The boat was pitching so crazily now that she shipped water in gallons, and there was nothing with which to bale. There was no pump, no compass, and no lantern; they were at the mercy of the tempest, and the oars were useless in the teeth of the gale. It was impossible to talk, because the words were torn away from the speaker's lips, and the force of the wind took the breath from their lungs. But Charles, cupping his hands, and roaring into the ears of Donald who sat above him, managed to make him hear that he thought they should put in to the shore.

" For I would sooner face all Cumberland's red-coats," he yelled, " than be out in a storm like this."

" We cannot be putting in to the shore," shouted Donald, " for the wind is against us, and the boat would be staved in pieces on the rocks."

" Then what must we do ? " cried Charles, almost in despair.

" Look you now," roared Donald (and somehow Charles knew that the old man was smiling), " since we are here, we have nothing for it but to trust in the Great Being, Who has the winds and the waves in His merciful hands. Is it not as good for us to be drowned in clean water as to be dashed to pieces upon a rock and to be drowned too whatever ? "

After this, nobody said a word, though the same thought was in the minds of all twelve of them, that inevitably they must be overwhelmed by the waves. The worst of it was there was nothing at all they could do. They could not row, or hoist the sail, they could not bale or steer. The wind had got them in its terrible hands, driving them whithersoever it pleased, the rain blinded them, and the crashing, tearing thunder made them deaf. Poor O'Sullivan was being dreadfully sea-sick, for he was a very bad sailor; as for O'Neil, when the lightning exposed him for an instant, he seemed to be gabbling prayers in a feverish, desperate sort of way which Charles was sure would not do any good. The

The boat was pitching so crazily now that she shipped
water in gallons.

others sat silent, grasping the thwarts to prevent themselves from being swept overboard with the lurching of the boat.

At last, at long last, the darkness began to lessen, and it was peep of day. Through the rain and the spray, Donald's keen eyes saw the shape of land ahead, and taking off his bonnet, he said aloud, without embarrassment, a prayer of thanksgiving to God Who had preserved their lives in that terrible storm.

" By the mercy of the Creator," he told the Prince, " we have not been driven upon the coast of Skye, as I feared we would be during the night, but have passed safely to the south of it, and yonder is the Long Isle, which is a great way from Scalpa whatever, yet since it is the country of Clanranald, who is loyal to your Royal Highness, we may land upon it and take some rest, and when the storm has ridden herself out, we may continue our voyage."

The wind had now changed about and was bearing them directly for the Long Isle. When they were come nearer and could see the nature of the coast, O'Neil cried out that they could never land upon such fierce rocks and were as like to be dashed to pieces as if they had attempted to turn back the previous night. But Donald smiled at him, and said that in the daylight it was a different matter, and that since the Great Being had brought them safely at least two and thirty leagues through the worst storm he had known in all his long life, he was confident that the Divine providence and his own intimate knowledge of this coast would guide them safely to their journey's end. And he was right. Though with very great difficulty, they did at last succeed in bringing the boat into a little bay on the shores of the island called Benbecula, which was part of the Long Isle; and, soaked, worn out, and faint from want of food, they set foot on dry land again after all those long hours of peril.

Benbecula formed the middle portion of the Long Isle, between North and South Uist. It was but five miles long and three miles broad, and was all barren moor, upon which there grazed the little shaggy black cattle of the Highlands; these beasts were so hardy that they could live on the poorest of feed. They lifted their long-horned heads at the sight of strange men dragging a boat up the rocks above highwater mark, but there was no human soul to witness the fugitives' arrival, for such houses as there were upon Benbecula were on the other side of the island.

Not far from where they had landed, they spied a bothie or hut, such as was used by herdsmen when they tended their cattle. Donald went forward alone to see if there was anyone there, and quickly returned to say that it was empty, and that it would serve them as shelter from the storm. So they went into it, and found it to be a most miserable little place, built of turfs and thatched with heather, through which the rain dripped in a dozen different places. Donald sent two of the boatmen to fetch the sail from the boat, that it might be spread on the floor and keep out the damp; meanwhile, he and his young son searched around until they had found two flints, and with these they struck a spark and lit with it some twigs of birch. From such unpromising beginnings did they contrive to make a fire in the bothie, though they had nothing for kindling but wet wood. The smoke was awful, but Charles was so glad to get a little warmth at last, that he fell asleep at once, curled up on the boat-sail.

When he awoke, he smelt cooking, and to his surprise found that Donald was stirring a sort of stew in an old iron kettle he had found in the hut. Donald smiled, and told him that on exploring the island, he and the boatmen had discovered a poor cow stuck in a bog, so they had killed her and put her out of her misery, and the meat from her would serve them for dinner. It was the toughest meat Charles had ever eaten in his life, for it was much too freshly killed, and besides, the cow was a very old one. There was nothing at all to go with the meat, so that altogether it was a horrible dinner, but when you are really hungry, any food tastes good, so when Charles had drunk a long draught of water, he began to eat very cheerfully.

"Surprise is upon me, your Royal Highness," said Donald, "that you should be so eager to drink before you have eaten, which is not at all the custom with my people, unless it be a dram of spirits."

"There is nothing that is better for the health, Donald," replied Charles between mouthfuls, "than a draught of cold water before breaking one's fast. You must know that I have taught myself to be something of a doctor, and a good doctor knows the value of simple things."

"For my part," chimed in O'Sullivan, "I value a bottle of good French wine more than all the cold water in the world." He sighed heavily. "When shall I taste wine of any sort again?" he concluded with another sigh.

By this time the storm had much abated, and Charles thought that they should continue their voyage. But Donald told him that he must have patience, for the oarsmen were still quite exhausted and the sea very troubled. As they had a long way to row before they could reach Scalpa, it would not be fair on the men, he said, nor would it be safe, to venture out again at present. Charles, who was always very thoughtful for other people, said at once that he was quite content to stay here until Donald gave the word to set out again, and he rebuked O'Sullivan quite sharply for saying that to remain in this place, with only stewed beef to eat and the rain coming through the roof, was unendurable and would certainly kill him.

"You will fare worse than this," the Prince told him, "if you share my hazard, for I have no doubt that before our wanderings are over, we shall have no food at all and no roof to shelter us. And now, Donald," he went on, "since there is nothing more we can do at present to ensure our safety, let us pass the time by having what

C

you call in the Highlands a ceilidh, for we all need cheering up."

In those days, people living in remote parts were forced to make their own entertainment as best they could, and the people of the Highlands never felt the want of books or stage-plays or things of that kind. During the winter months, when the days were short, and when storm and snow kept folk indoors through the long evenings, neighbours would gather together in one house, and there, sitting round the fire, with the women spinning or weaving or wool-carding, and the men smoking their pipes, they would have great fun. One of the company would play on the bagpipes, someone else would sing; the clarsach, or little Gaelic harp, would be passed round the circle for all to show their prowess with it, and then there would be stories, poems, and proverbs.

But with Charles and his little company upon Benbecula, the difficulty was that they had no pipes or harp, and also that none of the boatmen could speak English. However, Donald and Ned Burke took it in turns to tell those wonderful old stories which were handed down among these people from generation to generation, and which they never tired of hearing. They were chiefly tales of the ancient Caledonians, the people who had lived in the Highlands long before the birth of Christ. Great warriors they had been, and great hunters too, and since Donald and Ned like all Highlanders were very good at story-telling, they made the valiant deeds of old sound so thrilling that Charles listened entranced.

Between the stories, they danced a reel, one of the company whistling for them what was called the mouth-tune, which was a kind of mixture of humming and whistling, and suited the dance most excellently. And sometimes Charles would ask Donald and Ned to begin to teach him how to speak the Gaelic, for he felt sure that this would come in useful to him in his flight.

So there they stayed for two whole days, with one of them always on sentry-duty; and except for O'Sullivan and O'Neil, were not bored at all. They snared a moor-hen or two, and caught fish, so that they were not without food of a kind. And at last, on the evening of April 29th, they put out to sea again, and arrived safely at the tiny island of Scalpa early in the morning of the 30th.

3

The Bitter Disappointment

DONALD MACLEOD's friend, Donald Campbell, with his family and herdsmen, were the only people who lived on the tiny island called Scalpa, which was only a mile in length and half a mile in breadth; so for the present it formed a fairly safe retreat.

Mr Campbell and his family lived in a stone-built house, with an upper floor which was reached by a ladder, and here the weary Prince and his little company were most kindly entertained. They found the whole family very busy with mysterious preparations, and when Charles asked the reason for this, he was told that to-morrow was the Feast of Beltane, the first day of the Highland year, and there were certain customs which must always be observed upon that day. Rowan twigs must be fixed over all the doors to keep out evil spirits, the cows and all the other beasts must have a special blessing said over them to protect them against the spells of witches, and the children were given bannocks, marked on one side with a cross, which tomorrow morning they would roll down a hill to see which side

would be uppermost when they reached the bottom.
The Campbell family were so kind and hospitable to
Charles, that he felt he would not mind how long he
stayed here, so long as he did not endanger his hosts;
but Donald MacLeod told him that, in case the Militia
came to search the island, he himself would start off next
morning with his eight oarsmen, and sail to the port of
Stornaway on the big island of Lewis. For here, he
said, he hoped to find among the masters of the fishing-
brigs, some friend who might be persuaded to convey
the Prince to France.

Directly he reached Stornaway, Donald set about his
task, and a very difficult one it was, for he was reluctant
to entrust the Prince's secret to anyone save a man he
felt he could trust absolutely. As bad luck would have it,
none of the masters at present on the island was a close
friend of his, but after he had been in Stornaway for
nearly three days, he met a Captain MacAulay who had a
brig for hire. Donald did not know MacAulay very
well, so instead of telling him the real reason for his
wanting the brig, he said that he and some friends of his
wanted to make a voyage to the Orkneys to buy meal.
But MacAulay was suspicious and did not believe this;
he told Donald he was sure there was some other reason
for his wanting the brig, and that unless he would be
frank with him, he could not have it. So at last, despairing of finding another vessel, Donald made MacAulay
swear upon his dirk (which was called ' swearing on the
holy iron ', and was the most sacred sort of promise

37

known in the Highlands) that he would not disclose to any man what he was about to hear, and then he told him the truth.

MacAulay was at first very much taken aback, and said the whole thing was too risky. But now that he had told him, Donald dared not let him get out of it, so he bought MacAulay several drams of whisky, got him into a mellow mood, and at last obtained his promise to let him have the brig.

Full of joy, Donald sent Ned Burke back to Scalpa to tell the Prince the good news, and to guide him and his companions to Stornaway. Scalpa was very close to the island of Lewis, and at low tide it was possible to wade across the great tracts of sand which separated them from one another. Meantime, Donald made arrangements with a Mrs MacKenzie, a kind, loyal lady, who lived at Kildun House, two miles from Stornaway, to entertain the Prince when he arrived and until he could go on board the brig.

On the morning of May 5th, two days after he had sent Ned Burke to Scalpa, Donald met him by accident in the street at Stornaway. Ned said that the Prince had sent him to find Donald and to say that he and the two captains were at a certain spot on the moor close by, and that they would be very glad if Donald, when he went to meet them, could bring a bottle of brandy and some bread and cheese, because they had walked all night through pouring rain and were very cold and hungry. Ned confessed that, not being very well acquainted with Lewis, he had missed his way, and so they had travelled much further than they need have done. Donald bought the provisions and set out at once with Ned. Presently they saw Charles and his two companions crouching uncomfortably under a rock, partly to conceal themselves from any chance passer-by, and partly to shelter from the rain which was still coming down in torrents. They were all so tired and faint with hunger that they could scarcely return Donald's greeting; they were soaked to the skin, and their teeth were chattering with the cold.

" This stupid man," said O'Neil irritably, indicating Ned, " missed the way, and so I am sure we have walked no less than forty miles since we left Scalpa."

" Look at this ! " moaned O'Sullivan, holding up one foot to show how the sole had come off his shoe. " I curse the day that I am forced to walk in such intolerable discomfort."

" O'Sullivan," said the Prince quietly, " look at this." And then he held out both feet, and they saw that he had no soles on his shoes at all. " But thanks to you and honest Ned, Donald," he added, smiling, " we have arrived here safely, and soon, I hope, will cease to be a danger and a trouble to our friends."

After a dram or two of brandy and a piece of bread and cheese, they were all ready to complete their journey to Kildun House, though because they were so footsore they had to go very slowly. Good Mrs MacKenzie was at her door to welcome them; she burst into tears when she saw in what a miserable plight the Prince was, but he made light of it, and taking off his shirt, wrung the water out of it as though it had been a dish-clout, and hung it over a chair to dry before the fire. Having seen the fugitives sit down to a good meal, after which they would be able to go to bed and take some rest, Donald MacLeod set off alone for Stornaway, to make final arrangements for getting them on board the brig.

But as soon as ever he came into the little town, he saw that something unusual was happening there. The streets were full of people, and all the men were armed with some weapon, either a broad-sword or claymore, or a pistol or a dirk, or even some farm implement like a scythe. The women had left their washing and their baking, and were gossiping in their doorways; the trades-men had put up the shutters on their shops, and no one was doing any work at all. Even the old men had left their net-making, and had tottered out to mingle with the throng. Everyone was talking at once in the Gaelic, and all looked very frightened and angry.

Donald asked several people to tell him what it was all about, but no one seemed to know, and he could not get any sense out of them. They waved their arms at him and cried that they had been told by the chief townsmen that some terrible danger threatened the island, and that they must gather in arms and defend their homes and their boats and their cattle. After enquiry, Donald learned that these chief townsmen were just now con-gregated in the principal inn, conferring together on what they must do, so, as he knew most of these men, he jostled and elbowed his way through the crowds to the inn, and made so bold as to intrude upon the conference.

There were about half a dozen men in the room, all armed with the claymore and the Highland targe or shield, and with them was a piper, whose job it was to march ahead of his companions and inspire them with his music when they were going into battle. He was at present practising the *MacKenzie Gathering Rant*, striding up and down the room, punching the bag under his arm, and blowing through the drones which coughed and wailed in response. What with this, and the loud, confused talking of the others, the noise was so great that for a while Donald could not make himself heard. At last, however, one of the company observed him, and when he had made a signal to the rest, there was a sudden silence, and everyone turned to stare at Donald, very suspiciously and hostilely, as though he had been a stranger.

" What kind of a commotion is this you would be at, my friends ? " asked Donald in the Gaelic. " And why do you give me no greeting, I who am known to all of you, and have been a good friend to some ? What's the stir ?"

After a pause, during which they all exchanged glances, a Mr Angus MacKenzie, who was the general merchant of the little town, replied sternly :

" You do ill to ask such a question, Donald MacLeod,

seeing it is yourself who have brought this trouble upon Stornaway."

"What trouble is that?" asked Donald in astonishment.

"Captain MacAulay was after getting drunk last night," answered MacKenzie meaningly, "and he was telling those with whom he drank for what purpose you desired to hire his brig."

"Now a curse be upon him and upon all his race!" cried Donald, his black eyes flashing with anger. "Did he not swear to me upon the holy iron that he would keep secret what I told him?"

"The fruit of your wish be upon yourself, Donald MacLeod," retorted MacKenzie coldly, "for you have betrayed us your friends and neighbours in bringing the Prince upon us like a foe, with five hundred armed men at his back."

At this statement, Donald's anger gave place to such bewilderment that for a moment he could not speak.

"Did MacAulay tell you that the Prince had five hundred armed men upon Lewis?" he asked at length.

"He did," replied the other, "and he was telling us also that they will steal all our cattle and take all our boats for the conveying of themselves and their spoil to France."

"How," cried Donald, struggling between amusement and exasperation, "could you have been believing such a notion? Where, I pray you, could the Prince, in his present condition, get five hundred or even one hundred

42

men together? The knowledge is at you that he is a
fugitive with a price upon his head, that all his soldiers
were scattered at Culloden, and that he is hunted day and
night by the red soldiers. I believe you must be mad.
Has the Devil possessed you altogether?"

" MacAulay was positive of the truth of what he was
saying," insisted Angus MacKenzie.

" MacAulay was altogether drunk, and that on your
own showing," retorted Donald, " and will you be after
believing the idle tales of a man with the whisky in him,
rather than the assurance of myself, who have ever been
your friend? "

" That is as it may be," replied one of the others.
" But we are positive that MacAulay could not have been
inventing the whole story, and that the Prince is upon
Lewis."

At this, Donald paced up and down the room in silence
for a few minutes, trying to think what was best to be
done. At last, sighing deeply, he stopped and faced
them.

" Well, then," said he, lowering his voice lest he be
heard by someone outside the room, " since nothing will
satisfy you but the truth of it, I will acknowledge that
his Royal Highness is on Lewis; but then he is so far
from having any number of men with him, that he has
but three companions, and when I am there I make the
fourth. This is the truth. I swear it," he concluded,
very reverently and earnestly, " upon the Cross of the
Blessed One."

There was silence for a few minutes. They believed him, but they did not quite know how to act in the present situation. Then Angus MacKenzie, who seemed to be the spokesman for the rest, said, rubbing his hand across his bearded chin in a gesture of uneasiness :

" Understanding must be upon you, Donald, that no man who bears our name would ever stoop to the betraying of our lawful Prince, nor do we wish him any ill will. Yet we have our families and our homes to consider, and if we aid him we shall bring down upon us the vengeance of the red soldiers, who, from all we hear from the continent, spare none who have in any way assisted him. Therefore, we beseech his Royal Highness that he will immediately depart from our shores."

" And how may he be doing that," enquired Donald, his indignation arising again, " unless he have a ship ? "

" He shall not have a ship which belongs to the island of Lewis," asserted MacKenzie obstinately, " nor yet a pilot; neither of these shall he have though you offer five hundred English pounds for them. Let him go hence as he came, and our prayers and good wishes shall accompany him."

" My sorrow ! " exclaimed Donald, wrapping his plaid about him preparatory to taking his departure (for he saw it was useless to argue further with these men), " prayers and good wishes are cheap, and I am after thinking that when your children shall come to ask at you the story of this good Prince, you will wish you could tell them you gave him something more useful to him."

With that, he turned on his heel and strode out of the inn, and, pushing through the seething mob outside, went to collect his boatmen, since it was become plain that, wherever they decided to go next, they could not stay on Lewis any longer.

He found six of the eight boatmen in the small inn on the edge of the town where he had left them; the other two had run away because they had heard a rumour that the Prince and all his company were to be seized by the townsfolk. Those that remained were almost as scared as their companions, but at least they had not taken to their heels, and after Donald had told them that the Prince was leaving Lewis immediately, and that the best service they could do him and themselves was to man the eight-oared boat again, they expressed themselves as ready for the enterprise. So the six of them, with Donald, walked to Kildun House, and there the old man broke the sorrowful news to Charles. They found him sitting with Mrs MacKenzie and reading aloud to her while she spun wool on her distaff. His face fell when he heard the tidings; it was indeed a dreadful disappointment, just when he had been sure of getting safely away from Scotland. But when even stout Ned Burke burst out that the only thing they could do was to give themselves up, the Prince smiled his old cheerful smile at him, and asked :

" Since when, Ned, have you turned cowardly ? Captain MacAulay's brig is not the only one in these islands, and don't you fear but we'll find another one,

45

if God please. Meanwhile, Donald, what's to be done ? "

" I am thinking," replied Donald, scratching his bushy head, " that there is just one thing to be done at this time, and that is to return to Scalpa and stay awhile with Donald Campbell there."

" Very well," said the Prince briskly, " but it cannot be done tonight. For O'Sullivan and O'Neil are still so fatigued that they are fit for nothing, and I cannot leave them behind."

It was on the tip of Donald's tongue to say, that though the Prince was just as weary as his two friends he made no complaint, but the old man judged it wiser to hold his tongue on the subject. So they stayed another night with Mrs MacKenzie, though they did not sleep very much, for they were nervous all the time that the people of Lewis, if they chanced to discover that the Prince had not yet left the island, might make an attack upon them. At eight o'clock next morning, they said goodbye to their kind hostess, who gave them at parting two pecks of oatmeal, some brandy, and sugar, and other provisions in a little bag.

It was blowing a hard gale when they pushed off from the shore, but for once the wind was friendly to them, and helped them upon their course in the direction of Scalpa. All this coast was very dangerous with sand-banks, and the Prince suggested that it would be better for them if they stood further out from shore, but old Donald shook his head and said that sand-banks were less to be feared than the militia-boats, which, if they sighted them in the open sea, undoubtedly would catch them because such boats would have the greater speed. The oarsmen rowed in silence, still very depressed and nervous from the accident which had befallen them in Stornaway, but indeed conversation was almost impossible because of the noise of the wind and waves. Donald steered them skilfully, seeming to know every dangerous place, and after a while the boatmen grew calmer, and began to sing one of the boating songs which helped them to keep time with their oars.

After they had been rowing about an hour, and the Prince, sitting as formerly between the steersman's knees, was nearly asleep, suddenly he was broad awake at hearing from Donald a startled exclamation.

" What is it, Donald ? " asked the Prince anxiously.

" God be here ! " muttered Donald. " Will you be looking at that now ? " And he pointed to the open sea which lay to the east of them.

Charles looked; and his heart seemed to give a great leap in his breast. For there, perhaps about a quarter of a mile distant, no less than four fully rigged men-of-war were sailing, one behind the other. They were beautiful ships, their hulls carved and brightly painted, tier upon tier of canvas billowing from their masts; the little figures of seamen could be seen in the shrouds, and even from this distance it was possible to make out the ensigns and pennant straining in the wind from the mast-heads. But Charles was too worried to admire them; he could see the square ports along their sides, and he knew that when these were knocked open the wicked shining noses of cannon would be thrust through, for these were German George's fighting-ships, and at present they, like the red soldiers, were engaged in trying to capture him.

" Your black certain death-stroke to you ! " roared old Donald, shaking his fist at the ships. " The disease of old women that wind black thread at night be in your sides ! I have made my wish before, and I will make it again, and there was never yet a day when my wish was not fulfilled. My curse on you that seek to slay your lawful Prince ! " Then he became practical again, and, changing his course, shouted to the oarsmen to row directly for the nearest shore.

This proved to be a tiny island. It was, said Donald, uninhabited, for it was used as a burial island, and served as the cemetery for the people of Lewis. They grounded in a little creek, then dragged the boat out of sight behind some rocks, and themselves made all haste to conceal themselves in the heather. Charles tried not to think of what would happen if the look-out on one of the ships had seen them through his spy-glass; they could make a fight for it, of course, but there were only ten of them, and they had but two guns and their dirks. He lay still in the heather, and peeped through the tough brown stems at this, his first sight of the enemy since his defeat at Culloden.

He felt sure it would not be his last.

4

The Desert Island and the Man-of-War

UNTIL the fighting-ships had sailed away out of sight, they all lay as still as mice, with the rain pouring down upon them and the cold numbing their limbs. At last Donald wormed his way through the heather to the Prince's side, and told him in a whisper that he was going to make a tour of the island by himself, in order to make sure that there really was no one upon it, for sometimes, he said, the fishermen came here to dry their fish. By the time he returned, all their teeth were chattering like castanets from the cold, but he brought the good news that there was not a soul upon the island except themselves, and that therefore they could move about and make themselves as comfortable as possible.

" For," said he, " I am at thinking we shall need to stay here a while lest the ships return, for after this point upon our voyage to Scalpa we shall be obliged to put out farther from the shore than formerly, the rocks lying so thick that the boat would be staved in pieces if we sailed near the coast."

D

49

" But where are we to find shelter from this abominable weather ?" demanded O'Sullivan indignantly. " There is nothing here that I can see but tombstones, and besides that, the place is full of ugly great rats. I swear one of them ran over my legs just now."

" We will make a fire," returned Donald, " and we will be at eating some of the food which Mistress MacKenzie gave to us, and afterwards, Captain, you will think more cheerfully."

So saying, he began to organise measures for their comfort. He sent Ned Burke to catch some fish in a pool, and while he and his young son made a fire of sticks and turfs, the rest of the boatmen made a kind of tent with the boat-sail propped up on the top of stakes which they cut and drove into the ground. The Prince was very interested in all these activities, watching them and asking questions as eagerly as a child. The tent was just completed when Ned returned with a big flat fish which he had caught with his bare hands as it was lying on the sand at the bottom of a rock-pool. But he did not seem very pleased with his catch, though it was a fine one.

" Your Royal Highness," said he, " was pleased to appoint me your cook at Invergarry, but my grief ! I cannot be at cooking this fish unless I have some butter wherewith to dress it, for it has no natural grease as has a salmon."

" We shall get no butter here," said O'Sullivan, " and therefore undoubtedly we must starve."

" We will take the fish till the butter comes," said the Prince, smiling. " But since there are many of us, and we are all very hungry, do you, Ned, see if you can catch another one like it, so that we can enjoy a hearty meal."

Ned was going off on his mission, when suddenly he stopped, clapped his hand to his forehead, and exclaimed :

" Creator ! there's a foolish man I am. I am after remembering now that Mistress MacKenzie did give me a junt of butter among the food she put into the bag at Kildun House, and it will still be there in the boat."

" Which should teach you, O'Sullivan," said the Prince, laughing, " to have more faith in Providence."

So Ned ran off most joyfully to fetch the butter and to catch another fish. He was gone some while, and they were all growing impatient, being very hungry indeed, when he returned, but with such slow steps, and with such a doleful expression, that Charles called out to him :

" What, Ned, was the butter not there after all ? "

" It was there, your Royal Highness," replied Ned miserably. " But when we left Kildun I put it up with some bread in the bag, and the bread being now all crumbled in pieces, and wet besides, it has got among the butter, so that I think shame to present it."

" Was the butter clean when you put it among the bread ? " asked Charles.

" It was new-brought from the dairy, your Royal Highness," answered Ned, " though to be sure there were some cow's hairs mixed up with it, which indeed is usually the case."

" Then," said Charles, laughing heartily, " you are a child, Ned. If the cow's hairs cannot spoil it, I am sure good bread cannot do so. Come, hand me the wooden platter Mrs MacKenzie gave us, and let me show you how to make a right good dish."

So, borrowing a dirk, he filleted the fish, and put it on the thick wooden platter with some butter over the fire, which was smouldering and spitting without flames because it was composed of wet fuel, and presently the Prince bade everyone gather round a large flat stone which stood in the middle of their tent, and which, he said, would serve them for a table. The dish had not a very appetising appearance, for crumbs of bread were floating about in the melted butter, along with cow's hairs and one or two bits of seaweed which had got caught up with the fish; O'Sullivan took one look at it, shuddered, and said he would sooner starve than eat such disgusting food, but the others were too hungry, and too polite to the royal cook, to criticise. Before they began to eat, however, Donald MacLeod insisted that they should sit down in two separate companies, though it was still pouring with rain, and the tent, which was their only shelter, could not accommodate them unless they all sat down together.

" Among my people, your Royal Highness," said the old man, when Charles objected to this suggestion, " it is not the custom for lowly folk to sit down to meat with gentlemen of quality, and therefore, by your leave, the boatmen and myself shall sit by ourselves out yonder, while Ned shall wait upon your Royal Highness and your friends."

"Nay, Donald," protested the Prince, smiling, "it would be foolish to observe such customs upon a desert island, when hunger, thirst, and danger have made us all equal."

"Good manners, your Royal Highness," retorted the old man severely, "are to be observed under all conditions whatever, for if these are laid aside, it is but a step to the laying-by of good morals."

Seeing that Donald was very much in earnest, and would be hurt if Charles did not let him have his way, the Prince sat down under the boat-sail with the two captains (for when it came to it, O'Sullivan found that he was so hungry that he could eat the 'disgusting' food after all), while Donald and the boatmen took their portions to another stone out in the open under the pouring rain.

The date of their coming to this desert island was May 6th, and it was not until the 10th that Donald gave it as his opinion that it was safe to move on again.

It was a very uncomfortable period, for the rain continued to pour down, and though the flower-clusters of the cushion-pink were starring the rocks, and the nights were becoming mere grey twilights, with dotterel and golden plover calling, it was more like February than May. There was ice in the peaty pools, and when sometimes the dark sky lightened for a while, they could see the hills of Lewis, white with snow. They had to sleep on the bare ground, and though they had a fire it was always a poor one, and gave out more smoke than heat. It was melancholy, too, to live among the graves and tombstones, and the boatmen were very uneasy because, it seemed, they had a belief up here that the last person buried had to keep what they called the Watch of the Graveyard until another corpse arrived, and that those people foolish enough to stay on a burial island after dark, would be sure to see this ghost keeping its lonely vigil among the dust of its ancestors. Donald, too, was uneasy, but from a more practical cause; if a funeral procession chanced to come over from one of the neighbouring islands, he said, they would have to put to sea at once, whether there were men-of-war about or no.

Apart from the cold and the rain and the melancholy of the place, there were, as O'Sullivan had declared, a great colony of rats upon the island, huge things as big as cats, squeaking and scuttling under their feet as they walked through the overgrown grasses. One of the company had to stay on guard by their little horde of provisions, for otherwise the rats would have eaten the lot. Fortunately, thanks to kind Mrs MacKenzie, these provisions were still fairly plentiful, and besides there was plenty of fish. Every day the Prince used to take a run round the island, to keep out the cold and to retain his physical fitness, but O'Sullivan and O'Neil preferred to sit shivering and complaining under the boat-sail, reminding each other how miserable they were, and making themselves still more wretched by prophesying every kind of disaster in the future and recalling the comfort they had enjoyed, and the good meals they had eaten, when they were in exile in France.

One day, when Ned Burke was going to make some bannocks on hot stones by the fire, which he called 'birsling' them, the Prince asked him to bring some cow's brains which Mrs MacKenzie had given them, and which, because the weather was so cold, were still quite fresh. Then Charles showed Ned how to make a nourishing cake by mixing the brains with oatmeal, and then kneading them into a dough before baking. When it was cooked, the Prince broke the cake into pieces and gave each man a portion. To Donald MacLeod and the others it was marvellous to see this son of a king teaching simple men how to cook, and how he laughed and joked all the time, and seemed almost to enjoy the great hardships he was undergoing.

On May 10th they got into their boat once more, and set sail for Scalpa, telling each other how good it would be to see Donald Campbell again, and enjoy the comforts of his snug farmhouse after the cold and misery of the desert island. The short voyage passed without any excitements, but when they came trudging up to Mr Campbell's house on Scalpa, they found the door shut and even locked, a most unusual thing in the Highlands, where scarcely anybody ever locked his door. There was no smoke coming from the vent-hole in the roof, and when they had walked round the house and peered in through the windows, which had thin horn instead of glass, they could not see any sign of life.

"Donald," said the Prince fearfully, taking the old man aside, "do you think the red soldiers can have been here and killed Mr Campbell and his family?"

"The same thought was upon me," replied Donald, shaking his bushy head, "for it is death to all who shelter your Royal Highness."

For once Charles felt despair creeping upon him, when he thought of kind Donald Campbell and his family lying dead and perhaps unburied, with the eagles picking their bones, and all because they had aided him in his need. He felt he could not leave Scalpa without assuring himself of their fate, though Donald urged him to do so at once, because, for all they knew, the red soldiers might still be on the island. But Charles insisted on making a thorough search, and presently they found Mrs Campbell and her children hiding in a herdsman's bothie on the hill. The poor woman cried out when she saw them approach, supposing it had been the Militia, but when she saw who it really was, she sank on her knees before the Prince and begged him to leave Scalpa without delay.

"After your Royal Highness went from us," she moaned, "there was talk upon the island of Harris yonder that my man had sheltered you, and some who are not your friends there came threatening him, telling him that they would inform the Black Watch, so he has fled lest they come and seize him, and I dare not go home with my children until I am sure that it is safe."

Charles raised her up and tried to comfort her, but he was sadly aware that the best and indeed the only service he could do for her was to leave Scalpa at once, otherwise a new rumour might be started of his returning here, and so he would put her in greater danger than before. So he ordered his company to get down to the shore and into the boat again as quickly as possible, though they did not know in the least whither they could go, nor what course to set.

As it was clearly unwise to go northwards again, because that was in the direction of Lewis, they put the boat's nose towards the south, and, there being no wind, rowed cautiously along the coast of Harris, keeping a sharp look out for the Militia. At break of day next morning a wind sprang up, so that they were able to hoist the sail, which was a great relief to the oarsmen, who had rowed all night and were quite worn out. All this coast was very jagged and uneven, with many little bays and creeks and out-thrusts of land. They were sailing merrily along when, rounding a small promontory, they saw to seaward of them, not two musket-shots away, a man-of-war.

She was so close that they could see her name, the *Furnace*, painted on her hull, the seamen in their canvas petticoats and woollen caps busy on her decks, and the bright gleaming anchor secured to her bows. They saw too the device on her ensign which floated from the poop, and it was the black horse of German George.

" I will not be taken without a fight for it," muttered Charles, very white of face but resolute, as he turned to Donald at the helm of their little boat. " We have muskets and some dirks, and if the worst comes, we will use them."

" Oars are better weapons at present," replied old Donald wisely. " To your oars, boys ! Pull hard for the shore."

" It is useless ! " cried O'Neil, who was always quick to make the worst of any situation. " Now God have mercy upon us all, for she has spied us."

Indeed it was clear that the *Furnace* had sighted them, for at that moment they heard a shrill whistle sound from her deck, and a man with a speaking-trumpet ran to the gunwale and roared at them to pull at once to the ship.

" Pull for the shore, my brave boys," shouted old Donald to his boatmen. " Pull hard for shallow water, and we will be at beating her yet."

The oarsmen, though still very tired, responded valiantly. They rowed like demons, their bodies bending backwards and forwards so rapidly and strongly that the little craft seemed to fly through the waves. But they were a long way yet from the shore, and Charles, who had nothing to do but sit and watch the man-of-war, saw her sinister preparations for the chase. She was breaking out fresh sail, her seamen running up the rigging like monkeys to cut the gaskets of rope which secured the furled canvas to the yards; she had altered course, and stood directly astern of them; and he thought it impossible that with her speed she would not overhaul them in a very short while. He could hear the orders which the *Furnace's* master was shouting through his speaking-trumpet to the sailors aloft: " Haul aft the foresheet sail ! Veer the trusses; now hoist ! Top your topsail halyards, haul on your topsail sheets, slack out your topsail braces, haul out the topsail bowline ! " And then to the steersman : " Mate, keep full and by ! "

She was after them now under a full press of canvas, a beautiful, graceful bird of prey, towering above them and seeming as tall as a castle, the figurehead upon her prow, which was the likeness of a mermaid, dipping and curtseying as she came flying after them upon a favourable wind. Musketeers were swarming on her decks, and some of her seamen were getting ready the cock-boat, with which, while the musketeers covered the fugitives with their muskets, they were sure of seizing Charles and his friends.

" She's gaining on us ! " wailed O'Neil. " We'll never escape. They are priming their muskets, and we are almost within range. Best surrender before we have a volley of shot in our bellies."

" Wait you, wait you," soothed Donald MacLeod. " She'll be after finding the water too shallow for her in a moment, and then she'll be obliged to turn tail about, that big bully."

And he was right. Looking back at the *Furnace*,

" A mischief be in your side, you wolf ! " he yelled.

which had been so swiftly overtaking them but a moment before, Charles saw the seamen leave the cockboat in answer to the boatswain's whistle, and the whole ship's company set to work to stow some of the canvas they had just been hoisting.   For the experienced master of the *Furnace* had perceived that the water was become too shallow for the ship, and that if he continued the chase, she stood in danger of grounding or of striking a rock. With the feeling of being saved by a miracle, the desperate and weary crew of the little boat saw the man-of-war alter course again, and stand out from the shore.   Before she left, she sent a volley of small-shot whining and cracking from her deck in their direction, but they were now well out of range, and the bullets fell harmlessly into the water.

Then did old Donald, who had maintained throughout the hour of danger the greatest possible calm, relieve his pent-up feelings by standing up in the bows, and, shaking his fist at the *Furnace*, sent after her a string of his native curses.

" A mischief be in your side, you wolf ! " he yelled. " A bad meeting to you, you son of little men.   May the Son of Cursing take the souls of every man upon your decks, the eagle and the raven feast upon their bodies, and the fishes build their houses of your timbers !   May your crew wander for ever in the isle of the cold land, in thick, fenny vapours, never on hills or mossy vales of wind.   For the song does not record the name of the strong who wage war against the weak, and their fame shall not be heard.   Ach," he added, sitting down again, wiping his sweaty face with his hand, and smiling happily, "that has done them some ill and myself some good whatever; and now, boys, row into yonder creek and let us take our rest."

5

The Aimless Wandering

THEY dared not land upon the coast, for this was the island of Harris, and from what Mrs Campbell had told them it was plain that some of the inhabitants were unfriendly to the Prince. So they rowed into a little channel which was formed by two great rocks, and here, resting on their oars, they stayed till nightfall, being all the time in terror lest the *Furnace* send her cock-boat in search of them.

When the sun set and the twilight came, very cautiously they pulled out of their shelter, and saw that the ship-of-war had disappeared over the horizon. So they consulted together what next to do. It was plain that the peril threatening the Prince was becoming daily more terrible, for besides the men-of-war and the militia-boats and the soldiers and the Militia themselves, there were unfriendly islanders with whom to reckon. After much consultation, they decided that the only thing they could do in the present circumstances was to pursue their interrupted course towards the Long Isle, for at least it was a country of the loyal MacDonalds and they would

63

be as safe there as anywhere. There being a long stretch of open sea between Harris and the Long Isle, they ran the risk of encountering another or the same ship-of-war, but there were risks to be run whatever they did, and if they rowed all night, said Donald, they had a better chance of escaping in the semi-darkness, and ought to be able to make North Uist, the northern portion of the Long Isle, by morning.

Fortunately the wind was favourable again, so they hoisted their sail and presently were far from the land. It was very frightening to know there were no creeks handy for them if they encountered the enemy and were pursued, and they felt horribly defenceless, the ten of them, in that one little open boat. After they had been sailing for some while, O'Neil began to complain that he was terribly thirsty, and as soon as he said that, they all realised that they were not only thirsty but hungry as well, and that the provisions which Mrs MacKenzie had given them had all been eaten while they were on the desert island. Nor had they any fresh water.

" We ought to have brought water with us when we left the island," said O'Sullivan severely. "Heaven knows there was enough of it there; indeed it was about the only thing in which that miserable place abounded."

" I will give you the office of water-carrier next time," said Charles, " since you have nothing else to do but grumble, and then if you are thirsty you will have nobody to blame but yourself."

"Meanwhile, we must all die of thirst," moaned O'Neil. "I swear my tongue is as dry as a kiln."

"Then pray do not torment it with talking," said the Prince. "Now, Ned, as chief cook, I appeal to you, have we no provisions left at all?"

Ned rummaged in the bottom of the boat, and presently produced about a pound of oatmeal, which, he said, was all that remained in the bag given them by Mrs Mac-Kenzie.

"We could be at making dramach," said he, "but I am thinking the gentlemen's stomachs would not relish such poor fare."

"This gentleman's stomach would relish any fare at all," Charles told him cheerfully. "But pray, what is this dramach of which you speak?"

"Ach, it is nothing else at all, your Royal Highness," returned Ned, "than meal mixed into a paste with salt water."

"Well," said the Prince, "I confess that is a kind of dish I have never seen before, but it behoves me to try how it will go down, and therefore, Ned, do you prepare it, and I will be the first to sample it."

So Ned leaned over the side of the boat and brought up some sea-water in the iron kettle they had carried with them from Benbecula, and with this he mixed the oatmeal into a sort of mash. When it was ready, he presented it solemnly to the Prince upon his knees, for he was as strict about good manners as was Donald MacLeod, and never once forgot that the poor ragged fugitive whom he was assisting was the son of his rightful King. Charles scooped up a handful of the stuff and took a mouthful; they all watched him munch it, expecting to see him spit it out with a grimace. But instead, he finished the rest of the handful and then asked for more.

"While I have been among my friends here in Scotland," said he, in answer to their unspoken astonishment, "I have learned to take a share in everything, be it good, bad, or indifferent."

More out of politeness to him, than because even their hardened stomachs could fancy such food, Donald, Ned, and the boatmen took each a little of the dramach. But O'Sullivan and O'Neil would not so much as look at it; they sat watching the others make a gallant pretence of eating heartily, and kept telling each other how intolerable it was that fine gentlemen like themselves should be expected to eat such filth. After this had been going on for some time, old Donald, who had been giving the two captains some very sharp glances from under his bushy brows, suddenly drew himself up where he sat at the helm, and spoke thus:

"Your Royal Highness, it is your pardon I am asking if I make bold to address your two friends in a fashion which may not be altogether fitting from a poor Highlander to fine gentlemen. Look you now, sirs, you will have observed how, during all the time his Royal Highness has been upon his flight, never any meat or drink has come wrong to him, and that he has continued always cheerful and contented in any conditions whatever. His

Royal Highness was bred up in a king's palace, though it was in a land which was not his own; he has lived, as was his right, upon the best of fare, has slept in silken sheets, and if in his boyhood he endured the hardships of cold and hunger, he did so not from necessity but because he chose this method of hardening his body for great enterprises. Being forced at this time to endure the most bitter pains of hunger, cold, thirst, and the sickness bred by these, and likewise the perils of storms, tempests, and a merciless human foe, he behaves himself like a prince indeed; and did not our duty oblige us to serve him in all things as the son of our lawful King, our hearts would still bow down before him as a valiant hero, who shall be remembered and loved, whatsoever befalls him, by all the people of the Highlands, their children, and their children's children. But as for his two chosen companions, Captain O'Sullivan and Captain O'Neil, the song shall not recall their name, for though they be fine gentlemen, their spirit is that of the sheep."

After Donald MacLeod had ended this long speech, there was complete silence in the boat. The two captains sat beside each other on a thwart, facing Donald, as dumb as schoolboys rebuked by a stern master. There was something about old Donald, some simple dignity, which, at certain times, made one forget he was a poor old man who could neither read or write nor even speak English without difficulty, something so sincere and fine that now it had reduced O'Sullivan and his companion to a state of tongue-tied shame. Charles, regarding their reddened faces and fallen jaws in the light of the moon which had just risen, badly wanted to laugh; never in all the time he had known them had he seen them so crestfallen. But he knew it would most mortally offend Donald if he seemed amused by his lecture, so he bit his lip and said nothing; and so they sailed on in silence.

When the first grey light of day showed them their surroundings, the first thing they saw, but very dimly to the eastwards of them, was another man-of-war. She was much too far off for her to spy them; nevertheless, Donald said that they had best pull directly for the land. After standing up in the boat and taking a good stock of his surroundings, he said that the wind had carried them during the night the whole length of North Uist, and that they were come again to Benbecula. On Donald's advice, they did not land upon the island this time, but upon a tiny islet off it, and after hiding the boat as usual, set out to see if it was safe to make their camp here for a while.

All they found upon it was a grasskeeper's bothie, which was more like a pig-sty than a hut. The doorway was so low that the Prince, who was very tall, could not get through it, though he bent himself double, so Donald and Ned Burke dug up with their hands the loose wet earth beneath, which made it possible for Charles to crawl through on hands and knees; they put heather in the hole to make his passage easier. Inside, it was stuffy and damp and smelt awful, but this time even the two captains cheerfully laid them down to rest. The excitements and the exertion of the past few days and nights had made them all dead tired, and here at least they had some shelter from the weather.

When he awakened from a sound sleep, Charles looked around him at his companions and saw that Donald was absent. So he crawled outside and there he found the old man, muffled in his plaid, and walking up and down, evidently deep in thought.

" By your leave, your Royal Highness," said Donald in a troubled tone, " understanding is not upon me what next is to be done. I think it not safe that we should venture further upon the sea at this time, for those evil ones, the enemy ships, are keeping close watch around these islands, yet we cannot continue in this place, having no food."

" Besides food," said Charles, falling in beside him, " there is another thing lacking which I must have, and that is money. All I had is spent, for I will not have it said by man or woman that I ate their meat for nothing. I know how poor are your people, and because of their services to me I fear they will become even poorer in the future. Therefore, if I and my two friends may find some place of comparative safety where we may await your return, I would ask you to take the boat and make a voyage to the continent, where you could perhaps find out some of my richer friends who were with me formerly, and obtain from them the loan of some money, and even some advice as to what I must do to get a ship for France."

" I will do this willingly, your Royal Highness," replied Donald, " but it is my wound to think that there is no man hereabouts with whom I may entrust your safety while I am absent."

" Is there not, then," suggested Charles, " some lonely place in the mountains where we may lie secure without anyone being the wiser ? For we are all now accustomed to hardship and to living in the open air, and if it is a country where game may be shot, I will turn hunter and provide for the rest, for I am very skilful with the shot-gun."

Donald thought hard for several minutes in silence. Then he said :

" Such a place would be the mountains of Coradale in South Uist, where there is plenty deer, besides hares and moorfowl, and the people at this time of the year will not yet be at the shieling-huts."

" What are they ? " asked Charles.

" Ach, you must understand," replied Donald, " that in the month of June the young men and lassies of my people drive their cattle-beasts up into the mountains because the pasture is fine and sweet up there, and here they stay all summer long, tending their cattle and living in the little huts which we call shielings. Then when the leaves fall from the trees, they bring their cattle-beasts, which have grown as fat as butter, down to the glens again."

" These mountains will do very well for us while you are absent, Donald," said Charles.

" That's you ! " said Donald approvingly. " By your leave, you shall take Ned Burke with you for a guide, since he has the English and the rest can speak only the Gaelic, and I will take the boat and my oarsmen and sail straightway for the continent. When the tide is low, you may cross from Benbecula to South Uist upon the sands."

So it was agreed, and they went together into the bothie to inform the others of the plan. But before he would permit the Prince to set out on his long walk, Donald made a short excursion to Benbecula by himself, and when he returned he carried a bag of oatmeal, some shot for the two guns they carried, and two plaids in the MacLeod tartan. He would not say how he had obtained these things, and Charles, though he had a great respect for the old man, could not help wondering whether he had not helped himself to them from some house on Benbecula, for Donald and his people had their own ideas about honesty. There were certain things in the Highlands the people regarded as sacred and not to be stolen on any account; but there were other things, as for instance cattle, and especially an enemy's cattle, which they regarded as common property or lawful spoil. So Charles judged it wiser not to question Donald about these ' gifts ', but accepted them thankfully.

" The meal," explained Donald, " will make you bannocks and brose, though it is my wound that I was not after getting you some butter to go with it. The shot your Royal Highness will need for your hunting, and the plaid is the only dress for the hunter in this country, having many uses, as Ned Burke here will be explaining to you. I was not after fetching plaids for our two fine gentlemen, Captain O'Sullivan and Captain O'Neil, for I am at thinking they will not wish to hunt the deer."

He said this rather sarcastically, for he had taken a great dislike to the two captains, though since his lecture they had scarcely grumbled once.

Donald helped the Prince to put on one of the plaids, arranging it so that his right arm and his legs from the thigh were left bare, and keeping it firm round the waist with a piece of heather rope, because he had no belt to give him. To this rope he fastened a sporran or purse made of badger's hair, and dressed like this, with his beard grown because he had not been able to shave lately, Charles was better disguised than he had been since he began his wanderings, and also, when he set out on his walk, he found the dress very comfortable, for it left the limbs free and yet was very warm.

When he and Ned were dressed, they said good-bye to Donald and the boatmen, and, accompanied by the two captains, set out on their fifteen mile walk. All of it was over very rough ground, and there were many streams to ford. Because the weather had been so wet of late, these streams were in spate, tumbling and racing over their boulders in a very frightening manner, and boiling furiously in the pools. Ned showed his companions how to ford a stream in the Highland manner. He cut two stout sticks from a tree, gave one to the Prince and retained the other himself, and then, making them all join arms, he gave the word to step down into the water, the Prince and he feeling with their sticks to discover the depth before the next step was taken, and supporting between them their two nervous companions. Thus, going carefully step by step, they came safely to the other side.

They avoided the clachans and kept to the open moor, though here they saw a great many people, because this was the season for cutting peat. Whole families were encamped around the peat-hags, fathers, mothers, and children all working together to cut and dry the precious winter fuel. These people gave the travellers a courteous greeting, to which Ned replied in the Gaelic, but they were too busy to be curious about them, though they stared at the two captains in their English dress.

After they had been walking for a long while, Ned, who was in front, began to lead them up the side of a mountain, and after that it was all climbing, slipping and scrambling on the scree, as they called the areas of loose stones which formed the lower slopes of the hills, crawling along on hands and knees over rock which offered no secure foothold, and presently finding pockets of snow into which they sank ankle-deep. It was the time of the year when cracks and fissures appeared in the snow which covered the upper slopes, and when, with a dull and frightening thunder, great blocks of snow broke off and came tumbling down into the valleys. It was the first time Charles had climbed one of these Highland hills, though he had known the mountains of France from boyhood, and what with the sudden swirls of mist, the dark shadows of eagles falling on the snow, the roar of streams in spate, and the idea of being surprised by some of the Militia in his defenceless position, he found it very unpleasant. As for the two captains, except for their gasping breath and a groan or two, they were quite silent, having all they could do to keep up with Ned and the active Charles. Poor O'Sullivan, who was very fat and quite unfitted for exercise of this kind, suffered worst of them all.

At last, just before the sun set, Ned led them round an out-thrust of rock into what seemed a new world. They were come into one of the mountain corries, which were little valleys cupped in the arms of the hills, all clothed in sweet grass and herbs and bright with the earliest blooming hill-plant, the purple mountain saxifrage. Except for scattered drifts, the snow had already melted in this sheltered place, and though, being so high up, it was very cold, the air was sweet as wine. In the midst of this corrie lay a little lochan, the water glowing pink in the evening light, fringed with tall reeds, and very still. Near the lochan were some little round bothies made of turfs; these, explained Ned, were the shieling-huts, and since at present they were uninhabited, they would serve for shelter from the cold of the night. They cut branches of fir and pulled heather for their beds,

74

and when they had eaten some of their oatmeal, they lay down to rest after their long and exhausting climb.

They lived for three whole weeks up there in the corrie, waiting for Donald MacLeod's return. Except that he was very anxious for his own safety and that of his friends, Charles was happy, happier than he had been since his defeat at Culloden. For the weather suddenly cleared and became fine and almost warm; they saw no sign of the Militia, no sign of anyone at all; and the duty of providing food for his little company was a pleasure also, because all his life he had loved hunting better than any other sport in the world. Every morning at break of day, he and Ned would fill their pockets with meal, take each a gun, and set out into the mountains, leaving the two captains to amuse themselves as best they could. It was not a kind of hunting at all familiar to Charles, for they had no horses or hounds, and they must be absolutely sure of their fleet quarry before firing one of their precious shot. All the while, too, they were conscious that they themselves were being hunted, and that the noise of a shot might bring the Militia down upon them.

Charles found that Ned Burke was a good teacher and guide in this sport, for every Highlander was trained from boyhood to hunt the deer. After the long hard winter, during which they had lived in the glens, the red-deer were beginning to climb again, in search of the young grass, and were becoming increasingly shy and difficult to shoot. Ned taught Charles how to lie motionless for hours at a time, how to crawl on his belly through the heather as quietly as a mouse, and how always to keep to windward of the quarry, because a deer's sense of smell is very keen, whereas their eyesight is poor. It was very exhausting sport, and apart from the fatigue, Charles suffered greatly from the bites of the cleg, a kind of horse-fly, which infested the mountains. At first, when they settled on his bare arm or leg, he took no notice of them, for they made no sound, and in his ignorance he thought that they were just rather large house-flies. Then he would feel a terrific irritation, and found that they had raised great red blisters which afterwards prevented him from sleeping.

On some days, when they were stalking a deer from morning till night, they ate no food at all, but Ned taught him how to tighten his belt and so prevent faintness. He showed the Prince also how to find the heath-peasling, and this, when one chewed the root of it, took away one's hunger for the time. On other days they would mix their meal with water from a stream to make a thin brose, and they found this wonderfully sustaining. They had many small adventures, as once when Charles stumbled on the den of a wild-cat, and the next thing he knew he was being attacked by a veritable fury in the guise of a tabby coat with a black-tipped-tail, her sharp claws and teeth mauling him because she thought he was going to hurt her kittens.

At night they returned to their corrie, Ned carrying the spoils of their hunting, and then he would make the two captains assist him in skinning it and cutting it up. Besides the deer, they shot blue mountain hares, which were very tough and stringy, ptarmigan which tasted rather like turpentine because it lived upon the young shoots of the fir, and moorcock which Charles was most skilful in shooting on the wing. Sometimes Charles would have a day's fishing for a change. Ned made him a coble, or Highland boat, out of deer-hide stretched very cunningly over staves of wood, and in this frail craft the Prince would launch forth into the lochan, and with handlines catch the earthy-tasting brown trout that lived there.

Being continually in the open air, the exposed parts of his body became as brown as a berry, so that his fair hair and beard looked almost white by contrast. The two captains developed the most frightful colds, but Charles was fitter than he had been since Culloden. Sometimes sudden drenching rain would overtake him on his hunting, at others he would tumble into a burn, and at these times he realised how useful and suitable a garment was the plaid, for Ned taught him how to prevent catching cold by wrapping himself tight in the sopping blanket, rolling himself round and round in the folds, and then the warmth of his body, combined with the wetness of the plaid, would make a steam like a Turkish bath.

One day, when they had returned from their hunting, and were cooking collops or chops cut from a hind which they had shot, a very ragged boy, about twelve years of age, appeared suddenly and as it seemed from nowhere, round the corner of a shieling-hut, and, without a word, ran to the fire and seized a piece of meat from where it was cooking over the turfs. Ned, with a furious exclamation in the Gaelic, hit the boy's hand very smartly, and was about to drive him away when the Prince intervened.

"Ned," said Charles, "don't you remember that the Scriptures command us to feed the hungry and clothe the naked? You should give this poor lad food rather than a stripe."

He took a piece of meat and gave it to the boy, asking him whence he came and who he was. The boy snatched the food and glared at him like a wild-cat; then, still without speaking a word, he ran off and disappeared as mysteriously as he had come.

"I am not after liking this at all, your Royal Highness," said Ned, staring after the intruder. "Fear is upon me that this rude one will be talking to his friends about our presence here."

"What has he seen but a party of hunters?" asked Charles. "That is no unusual sight among these mountains."

"There are some amongst us who do not look like hunters whatever," muttered Ned, glancing with distaste at the two captains. And indeed, O'Sullivan and O'Neil, in the ragged and travel-stained uniforms they had worn since Culloden, did not look like anything but the fugitives they were.

It was about three days after this that they heard someone imitating the cry of the willow-warbler, and hastened to meet Donald MacLeod. He looked grave and worried; he had left the boatmen with the boat in a creek, he said, for in his opinion the Prince and his company ought to leave South Uist without loss of time. The Militia were landed on the island, and were hunting everywhere for Charles; he did not understand how it was, but they seemed to have received certain information of the Prince's presence here.

"Now my sorrow!" exclaimed Ned, when he heard this, "but right I was after all, and it was that cursed boy gave us away. Was I not after telling your Royal Highness how it would be?"

"Yes, you were, Ned," admitted the Prince. "But it is no use crying over spilt milk, as they say, and we are fortunate that he has not yet guided the Militia to our retreat. And now, Donald, what luck had you in obtaining any money for me, and what news did you hear upon the continent?"

"Ach," said old Donald ruefully, "I was not after getting more money than would buy a little brandy and other stores, for the gentlemen I found who are friends of your Royal Highness are as desperate fugitives as yourself. As for the news, it is not good whatever. There was a French ship came in to Arisaig, and took off the Duke of Perth and other lords and gentlemen, but they not knowing in the least what was become of your Royal Highness, judged it useless to wait upon your coming, and indeed the master of her would make no

79

long stay, lest he be taken by the enemy's men-of-war. Besides all this, the Militia are everywhere, as thick as midges at the sun-setting, and it is my wound to think that I know not whither I may counsel you to go next."

" We must entrust ourselves to the mercy of God," said Charles, as cheerfully as he could, " Who up to this present has not failed us. Let us first get to the boat again, and when we are away from South Uist, we will consult what we must do."

It was now the 6th of June, and for several days and nights thereafter they cruised up and down the Long Isle, not daring to land anywhere, and often having to row hard into a creek to escape being sighted by a man-of-war. Sometimes Donald would slip ashore by himself to find out the news, and always he returned looking more worried than ever, because he heard that the hunt after the Prince was growing hotter and hotter, both by land and by sea. There was a whole squadron of war-ships after him now; the frigates *Greyhound*, *Baltimore*, *Terror*, *Scarborough*, *Glasgow*, and *Furnace*, and the sloops *Raven*, *Trial*, and *Happy Janet* were scouring the coasts of the Long Isle, for it seemed that the enemy was positive that Charles was in this neighbourhood. The Prince and his companions sailed right down to the foot of the Long Isle, and landed on the shores of Loch Boisdale, hoping that the local chief, who was a loyal man, would be able to give them assistance, but they found that he had been taken prisoner, and so there could be no refuge there.

For the past week, Charles had become very silent and thoughtful, and after they had left Boisdale again, he said to Donald MacLeod :

"It is plain that we cannot continue as we are at present, for sooner or later, if we go on cruising up and down these islands, we shall be taken. There is but one chance I can see and that is to separate, for if the enemy has information of our whereabouts, he will know also the names and number of our company."

"That is the truth that is in it, your Royal Highness," answered Donald promptly, "and so I would advise that you part company with Captain O'Sullivan and Captain O'Neil and leave them to take their chance with the boat-men, while you and I may make our way by land to North Uist, where we may try to get us a boat for the continent again."

But Charles shook his head.

"No, Donald," said he, "it is you and I who must part, for if they captured you in my company they would kill you, and I could not bear that. With O'Neil and O'Sullivan it is otherwise, for they have been in the service of the King of France, and because of this it is possible they might escape death if they were taken. Now you will have seen that these two gentlemen, and especially Captain O'Sullivan, are not very good at skulking, yet they are my friends, and I am responsible for their safety. Therefore, do you take O'Sullivan under your care and do the best you can for him, and I will take O'Neil. He and I will find our way somehow to North Uist, and trust in Providence to send us some friend there who will convey us back to the continent. For though the soldiers and the Militia are everywhere, these islands, being so small, are the more dangerous."

Donald was very sad and worried by this resolve of the Prince, and argued for some time, but he knew in his heart that the only chance for all of them was to break up their company; if they stayed together they would all be taken, whereas if they parted, perhaps some of them would escape. In any case, the Prince had quite made up his mind, and there was no moving him. He bade Donald put in to the shore again, and there, assembling the little company around him, he ordered O'Sullivan, to whom he had given his money when he had any, to write down, with a burnt stick upon some pieces of an old shirt, a note saying that he, " Mr James Thomson ", owed each of the boatmen one shilling a day for their services for all the time they had been with him, and another to Donald MacLeod promising him sixty guineas when he was able to pay him. He dared not put his own name in case Donald and the boatmen were captured and the notes were found and used in evidence against them. Neither Donald nor the boatmen wanted to accept the notes, because what they had done for their lawful Prince had been not only a duty but a pleasure, but Charles insisted, saying he would be hurt if they refused. Then he gave them each in turn his hand to kiss, and in a broken voice he thanked them for all they had done for him.

"The hand of your valiant ancestors be over you," murmured old Donald, when it came to his turn and he, upon his knees, had laid his lips upon the Prince's weather-stained fingers. "May a straight path be before you, and a happy end to your journey, and as you go from us in sorrow, may you return in joy."

Then his voice was choked with tears and he could say no more. Indeed every man of them, including the Prince, was so upset by this sad parting, after being so long a time together, and having shared so many dangers and narrow escapes, that not one of them could find much to say. So Donald and Ned, with O'Sullivan and the boatmen, stood in sorrowful silence and watched the lonely figures of the Prince and Captain O'Neil stride away over the heather, thinking it impossible that they would ever meet again. Charles had no protector now except God, no guide except the sun and stars, no friend except the inadequate O'Neil, no shelter, plan, or destination unless Providence would provide them.

6

The Gallant Lady

THE Prince and O'Neil walked all that day, going steadily northwards across the Long Isle.

They had to cross many fords, sometimes being obliged to wait hours for the tide to recede, and then wading and splashing over the white sands where large silvery eels waited for the tide to return. The weather was stormy, sometimes fine and bright, at others dark with rain, and it was still so cold that it was surprising to see the bell-heather blooming purple and the wild roses wreathing the moors. They avoided the clachans, and once had to dive down behind some rocks to escape being seen by a company of the Militia, who, with red crosses and black cockades in their bonnets, were searching the neighbourhood. At night, quite tired out, and not knowing in the least where they were, they began to feel that unless they had some food and shelter they would not be able to go on.

Presently they saw in front of them a solitary light which betokened a habitation of some sort. They dared not approach it without discovering something about it, since for all they knew it might be full of the Militia. So O'Neil who, though he was too faint-hearted to be of much use to his Prince, yet was very loyal and anxious to do what he could, especially as Charles had now no other companion, offered to go on alone and discover whether it was safe to seek shelter at the house.

When he got to the light, he found that it came from a little inn, or change-house as they called it in these parts. Like all Highland inns of those days, it was very small and poor, being used chiefly by drovers and herdsmen. It was really only a cottage, with a byre or cow-shed attached to it on one side, and a little stable on the other. O'Neil peeped into the stable, and saw that there was a shaggy Highland pony in there, munching a meal of bog-hay. This seemed to indicate that the landlord might have a guest, and he wondered if it would be wise to enter the inn after all, but then he remembered how dead tired Charles was, and how faint with hunger, so he decided to risk it. Like many timid men who are good at heart, O'Neil, when he was left on his own and was therefore forced to take decisions, discovered an unexpected boldness.

So he knocked upon the door and entered the change-house. The door opened directly upon the living-room, and here he found the landlord and his family, together with a stooping, rough-looking man with very long black moustaches and great eyebrows, which gave him a most fierce expression, seated round the table and eating their supper. They were all chattering in the

Gaelic, and O'Neil, who could not speak a word of it, wondered how on earth he was going to make himself understood. However, he was relieved to find that there were no Militia here, and that the surly-looking man, who presumably was the owner of the pony, went on eating and took no notice of his entrance. By elaborate signs, O'Neil managed to make the landlord understand that he desired some food and could pay for it (as a matter of fact, he had no money at all, but he felt that if he got the food first he could explain that afterwards), and the landlord, pointing to an upturned butter keg, gestured to O'Neil to sit down and help himself.

O'Neil was just beginning to eat a toasted calf's ear, and was wondering how he was going to conceal some of it to take to the Prince, when suddenly the man with the fierce eyebrows said to him in English :

" An honourable death be yours."

Now, this was a very common expression of civility in the Highlands, and was often used by way of greeting. But as O'Neil did not know this, it sounded very ominous to him, for he had no desire at all for death, be it honourable or otherwise, though he thought it likely that if the Prince and he continued to wander about as they had today, he would be dead very soon. So he merely gaped at the man, not knowing what to say in reply.

" It is not very often," continued the surly stranger, " that we see those of your country in these parts, except the red soldiers," and with that he spat viciously into the fire.

This encouraged O'Neil, since it was plain that the man was no friend to the soldiers. So he said that he and a friend of his had travelled far that day, and had quite lost themselves, and then he asked him what place this was. The man gave him some Gaelic name, which sounded like something between a cough and a sneeze; then, suddenly, he said something in Gaelic to the landlord, who, signalling to his family, took them out into the kitchen and shut the door, leaving O'Neil and the stranger alone.

" The thought is on me," said the stranger, taking out a very foul pipe and filling it with tobacco from his sporran, " that you may be of his Royal Highness his company, and you must know that I am the servant of one who has the Prince his welfare very much at heart."

" And who may that be ? " asked O'Neil warily.

" Mistress Flora MacDonald," replied the other, raising his bonnet at the name, and jerking his head towards one of the wicker partitions as if to indicate that the lady was in there. " Myself am called Neil MacKechan, and I am at escorting Mistress Flora on a journey to visit her brother at Milton. Being overtaken by the night, we were needing to stay at the change-house here."

At the mention of a lady, Captain O'Neil's spirits had risen considerably, for he was very fond of the ladies, and he was vain enough to believe that they were all very fond of him. He was quite a handsome young man, and had what is called a way with him; he was very good at paying pretty compliments, and he was firmly convinced that this gave him right of entrance to every woman's heart. However, he managed to remember that at present his business was to secure food and shelter for his Prince, so he asked with assumed carelessness :

" And how does it come that this Mistress Flora MacDonald has his Royal Highness's welfare at heart ? "

The man seemed affronted by the question.

" And what would she have otherwise whatever ? " he demanded, " and she the most gallant lady in the Isles. Ach," he added, in a different tone, " she was after dancing with him at a ball in Edinburgh when he was upon his march south before this terrible battle of Culloden, and was so charmed with him that she has been quite taken out of herself."

" Pray present me to Mistress Flora," said O'Neil, delighted, " that I may have some talk with her."

MacKechan rose at once, and going to the wicker partition, spoke through it in Gaelic to someone in the other room. After a few moments, the door in the partition was pushed open, and a young lady came through.

She was a healthy-looking Highland girl, dressed in a cloth gown and petticoat, with a plaid over her shoulders, a silver brooch at her neck, and a red ribbon confining her long black hair. Though she had a kind, sensible face, she was not at all beautiful, but O'Neil, who had not seen any women of late except the poor ragged ones of the clachans, whose faces were always black with peat-smoke, thought she was as lovely as a princess. He brushed back his unkempt hair, straightened his dress, made her a low bow, begged leave to introduce himself, implored her to pardon his boldness, and, taking her by the tips of her fingers, escorted her to a chair by the hearth as though she was incapable of walking there unaided.

"Allow me to inform you, Miss," said he, taking up what he thought was a graceful attitude before her, "that I have the misfortune to be a fugitive, having served in the army of a certain Gentleman who at present I forbear to name. Therefore I beg of you to let me know what are my chances of obtaining a boat to transport me to the mainland, for I hear that I am in great peril while I remain in these islands."

"I doubt you'll get to the continent without being captured by the Militia," replied Flora calmly, "since all the coasts are guarded, and a great search is being made upon the Long Isle, as myself should know, seeing that my stepfather, Hugh MacDonald of Armadale, commands one of the companies of the Militia. You must not take me wrong, sir; his heart does not set with the red cross in his bonnet, and he is a very honest man, but he has taken German George's wages and knows his duty."

She was looking O'Neil up and down as she said this, not rudely but with the native curiosity of her race.

Noting this, he supposed that she had fallen in love with him at first sight, and began preening himself the more. Actually she was thinking how comical he looked, with his unshaved face and his ragged dress and the airs he gave himself. Sustained by his own vanity, O'Neil decided that he could trust her to the uttermost, and so, leaning towards her and speaking very low and impressively, he said :

" You must know, Miss, that I have a friend with me in my skulking, and I am told by your servant that this friend's welfare is dear to your tender heart."

The girl looked at him quickly at that, caught her breath a little, and, with flushed cheeks, asked abruptly :

" Do you mean the Prince ? "

" He is not two hundred yards from this house," replied O'Neil, " hiding in the heather."

" God be here ! " murmured the girl. " And the Militia thick upon North Uist." Then she frowned, and added reproachfully : " Is his Royal Highness out alone there in the night, while you and I are warm by the fire ? "

" I will go and fetch him at once, if you please," said O'Neil eagerly.

" You must not do that," said Flora, rising and pacing the room in great agitation, " for the knowledge is not at me whether the landlord here be honest." She paused and spoke for some while in the Gaelic to MacKechan. Then she turned again to the captain. " But you must not leave his Royal Highness unattended any longer,

and you must be at taking him some food. If you have
no money, I will pay the charges, but pray let haste be
on you to return to him."

" Though he is hungry," replied O'Neil, " he is more
in need of a plan whereby he may get off these islands, and
I beg of you, if you love him, to aid him in this."

" I have thought upon it," said Flora impatiently,
" and I believe I could convey him to my mother's
house in the island of Skye, but for this I should need a
pass, lest we be questioned by the Militia. I do not
know whether I could get one from my stepfather, but
I will try. Meanwhile, he must lie hidden in the neighbourhood and watch for my return. I cannot promise
that I shall be able to aid him, but you have my word
that I will return and let him know whether I can do so
or not. Here is some money, sir; buy food and drink
and take them to his Royal Highness, and carry my
servant MacKechan along with you, that he may inform
me where I shall find the Prince when I return."

With this, O'Neil had perforce to be content, though
he did not think it very satisfactory. However, he was
convinced that Miss Flora was by this time fallen so deep
in love with him that she would think out a plan for his
safety. He bought meat and brandy with the money
she gave him, and set out with the surly MacKechan to
the place where he had left the Prince. MacKechan,
having marked the spot, went off again, with the long
loping stride of his race, to rejoin his mistress.

All next day, and throughout the following night, the

Prince and O'Neil lay hidden in the heather, waiting and watching for Flora MacDonald to keep her promise and come and fetch them. They were in a sad plight, for if she failed them they did not know what they could do, and besides this, the food which O'Neil had brought from the change-house was finished, and as they dared not venture out from their hiding-place to beg for more, they had nothing at all to eat and only water from a burn to drink. It was very lonely there; they watched the people from the change-house tethering their sheep and goats in the out-field, the woman washing blankets in the burn, and her husband digging with a wooden spade in his in-field, and this peaceful, homely routine only made them feel their own sad plight the more. They envied the heron which, every day, came to fish at a pool near by, standing there motionless for hours, and, with his humped shoulders, and his murderous beak hidden in his breast-feathers, looking very like a tall old gentleman in a grey, tailed coat.

At first O'Neil was very confident that Miss Flora would keep her promise and return to them, saying that it was obvious she was fallen deep in love with him. He did not know how it was, he said, but every woman who looked at him lost her heart to him at once. He was sorry for this poor Highland girl, for when she had got him safely out of the country, he was sure that she would pine away and die because she could not go with him. But after a while, when no Flora appeared, he changed his tune and began to say he was certain she had failed them, that they ought never to have trusted a woman, that in all probability she had betrayed them to the Militia, and that if she returned at all, it would be only to arrest them. The Prince listened to all this in silence, for he felt that if he spoke he might be tempted to tell O'Neil exactly what he thought of such foolish talk.

On the morning of June 23rd, two days after O'Neil had met with Miss Flora at the change-house, the Prince and he heard from some distance away a man whistling softly the Jacobite song, *Over the Water to Charlie*. Cautiously raising their heads from the heather, they saw that it was MacKechan, and hasted to meet him. He had brought some cold venison and some bannocks wrapped up in a napkin, and while they ate it, he explained to them why he had been so long in coming back, and also why he had returned without Miss Flora. It seemed that his mistress, on leaving the change-house, had ridden towards the house of her friend, Lady Clanranald, in order to enlist her help in aiding the Prince, but on the way she and MacKechan had been stopped by some of the Militia at a ford, and the men had taken them to the guard-house and had detained them there until the captain of the company had come to question them. By the greatest good fortune, this captain had turned out to be none other than Flora's stepfather, Hugh MacDonald of Armadale, and he not only had released them, but, having heard Flora's story, had agreed to let her have a pass which would enable her to cross over to Skye without being hindered by the Militia.

" This pass," continued MacKechan, " is made out for Mistress Flora herself, a man-servant, and a maid, and I am ordered to conduct your Royal Highness to Rossinish upon the north end of Benbecula, where Mistress Flora will have a boat in waiting to convey your Royal Highness over to Skye."

" I suppose, then," said the Prince, " that I am to play the part of Miss Flora's man-servant ? "

" Not at all," replied MacKechan. " The man-servant is myself, and your Royal Highness will be the maid."

" The maid ! " echoed Charles in dismay. " Do you mean that I must dress up as a woman ? "

" Right you are there," replied MacKechan cheerfully. " And for this purpose has Mistress Flora gone on to the house of Lady Clanranald to get some woman's clothes for you, and MacDonald of Armadale has given her a letter for her mother to say that he is sending her an Irish girl, one Betty Burke, who is a good spinster, and will spin all the wool she requires."

" Spin ! " gasped Charles. " I cannot look like a woman, much less can I handle a distaff."

" And what about me ? " cried O'Neil, before Mac-Kechan could reply. " What arrangements have been made to convey me over to Skye ? "

" I am not knowing that whatever," answered Mac-Kechan indifferently. " The trouble that is upon me is how we are to get to Rossinish, since we must be crossing much water between here and there, and all the fords are guarded. But we will go down to the shore, if you please, and there we will take our chance at hiring a boat, that we may make part of the journey by sea."

On the shore they were fortunate enough to find a girl gathering dulse, which was a kind of seaweed used by the people of the Highlands for making a very rich soup. MacKechan, after urging Charles and O'Neil to keep their mouths shut, approached the girl and talked to her for some time in the Gaelic, and after a while returned to the others and told them that he had persuaded her to lend them a small boat which belonged to her brother who was in hiding from the Militia, and he had promised to bring the boat back to her as soon as he could. It was a short voyage and they made it quickly, because Charles helped MacKechan with the rowing, and when they had landed safely on Benbecula, and MacKechan had hidden the boat where he was sure of finding it again, they set out to walk to Rossinish. The long Highland twilight was come when they approached a little house there belonging to one of Clanranald's tenants; this was the appointed meeting-place with Flora MacDonald, and MacKechan said that he would go in first and discover whether it was safe for the others to approach.

He was back very shortly with the terrible news that that very morning a company of the Militia had pitched their tents within a quarter of a mile of the house upon the other side, and had arranged to call there every morning while they were in the neighbourhood, to fetch milk for their breakfast.

"Great heavens!" cried O'Neil, on hearing this, "the Militia within a quarter of a mile of us, you say? Let us flee at once, or certainly we shall be taken."

"And whither shall we flee?" asked the Prince. "We must keep our tryst with Miss Flora, and it is only through her that we have any chance of escape at all."

"She may not come," moaned O'Neil, "in fact I am sure she will not come when she learns that the Militia are so close. What fools we were to have trusted in a woman, and a Highland woman at that——"

He was interrupted by being suddenly and violently flung to the ground with such force that the breath was knocked out of his body. To his horror he saw Mac-Kechan bending over him, with his dirk drawn and held with its point at the captain's throat. The Highlander's face was distorted with rage, from beneath his beetling brows his eyes glared fierce and terrifying, and his lips were drawn back over his teeth in a snarl.

"Now the place of the dead be yours, you son of swine!" screamed MacKechan. "The thought is on me that before I put my dirk into that filthy throat of yours, I will cut out your tongue that has so insulted my mistress and her race." At this, despairing of expressing himself properly in a language which was foreign to him, MacKechan lapsed into a spate of Gaelic.

O'Neil was so terrified that he could not speak, but he rolled his eyes in the direction of the Prince, silently beseeching aid. Charles, who knew something of the

O'Neil was so terrified that he could not speak, but
rolled his eyes in the direction of the Prince.

Highland people by this time, how quick they were to take offence if anyone insulted them, and how little regard for human life they had on those occasions, did his best to soothe MacKechan's injured pride by laying his hand upon the man's shoulder and saying quietly :

" Captain O'Neil spoke without thinking, my friend, because, like me, he is very anxious and very weary. As for me, I do remember how my great-uncle, King Charles the Second, owed his life to a lady when he was escaping after the Battle of Worcester, and how faithful and true she proved in this service. I am sure that Miss Flora MacDonald will be the same, and to show you how sure I am of it, I am content to stay here, within a stone's throw of the Militia, until such time as she comes to keep her appointment with me."

" Your Royal Highness is a great gentleman," replied MacKechan, not at all mollified and still retaining his hold upon the captain, " but as for this son of little men, this black-hearted coward, you and all of us will be the better without him, for he is no good whatever. I will dispatch him quickly and leave him here for the raven and the buzzard to have their feast on his flesh." And with that he raised his dirk.

" As your lawful Prince and master, MacKechan," said the Prince sharply, " I order you instantly to release Captain O'Neil and to do him no injury whatever. And him I do command to make full and frank apology for what he has said regarding Miss Flora MacDonald."

The air of authority which Charles knew very well

how to assume at the proper moment had its effect. Very reluctantly, and muttering angrily to himself in the Gaelic, MacKechan released his hold upon his intended victim, after which O'Neil, scrambling to his feet, his face ashen and his knees shaking, stammered an apology for having doubted Miss Flora's fidelity.

" And now," said the Prince briskly, " since it is night, I shall make bold to enter the house and take a few hours' rest before the time comes when the Militia will call for their milk. You shall keep watch for me, MacKechan, awaken me when the dawn breaks, and then convey me to some hiding-place near the house."

The people of the house were in a great state of panic, because they had been told who Charles really was, and with the Militia so close at hand, they were terrified of entertaining him, both for his sake and their own. But his calm courage shamed them, and persuaded them to give him and his companion food and a bed upon the floor. In the grey light of dawn, MacKechan aroused the two fugitives, and, without a word, led them out of the house and down to the sea-shore. As they went, they heard from some little distance behind them the pipes of the Militia playing to awaken the men to their new day's duty, and MacKechan cursed them under his breath.

At the edge of the shore there were some great rocks, some of them hollowed out and carved into fissures by the weather. At MacKechan's direction, Charles and O'Neil crawled into one of these crevices, and when

MacKechan had walked all round the rock and had viewed it from every possible angle to make sure that the fugitives could not be seen, he went off to watch for the coming of Flora MacDonald.

It was raining again, a thin, miserable drizzle, and crouched down there in the fissure of the rock, the Prince and his companion were soon wet through. They were used to this by now, but they were not used to so narrow and confined a hiding-place, and because they dared not move, their limbs soon became cramped and numb. It was the most uncomfortable of their concealments so far, and as the day wore on they found it almost unbearable. For there came swarms of midges, such as infest the Highlands during the summer months. These tiny insects settled on the exposed parts of their bodies, especially upon their eyes, raising a dreadful irritation and making their eye-lids puffed and swollen. So close were the Militia, and so ignorant were the fugitives of the position of their sentries, that they dared not so much as lift their hands to drive the midges away. Charles found that added to all his other troubles was the fear lest O'Neil, always faint-hearted, should give way under the torment and betray them both, but the captain was in fact so shaken by his narrow escape from death at the hands of MacKechan, that he bore his present discomfort with the most unusual patience.

All day long the Prince and his companion stayed in their horrible hiding-place, listening to the Militia talking in their camp, the rattle of their muskets, and the

voice of one of them giving orders to the rest. When
night came, MacKechan returned to take them back to
the house for some sleep. He had seen nothing of Miss
Flora, he said, nor had he had any word from her, but
he was still quite sure that she would come as she had
promised, and he glared at O'Neil, daring him to contra-
dict him. Next day they must go down to the rock
again, and endure the torment of midges and cramp for
another twelve hours. The day afterwards it was the
same; but during the afternoon, MacKechan stole down
to them with the news that the Militia were striking
camp and would be away by night. Sure enough, they
heard through the twilight the pipes strike up a march;
and scarcely had the music faded into the distance before
the fugitives, peeping out of their hiding-place towards
the sea, saw a boat approaching, rowed by four men, and
with two female figures seated in the stern.

Charles was so overjoyed at this sight that he could
not prevent himself from immediately crawling out from
his concealment and running down the shore, though for
all he knew the Militia might have left some of their
men behind to watch the place. He found he was so
stiff after three days' crouching in the fissure that he
could not walk upright; his feet had pins-and-needles,
and he felt dizzy and rather sick. But he hobbled as
quickly as he could to the water's edge, and there he
greeted Flora MacDonald who was being carried out of
the boat by one of the oarsmen. She was much moved
at seeing him again, and in so different a guise from that

he had worn when she had danced with him at Edinburgh, but being a sensible girl she did her best to hide her emotion, which could do him no manner of good. Having greeted him without any recognition of his rank, she presented the other lady, her friend, Lady Clanranald.

This good woman, who was not quite so discreet and self-controlled as Miss Flora, as soon as ever she was presented to the Prince, sank into a deep curtsey on the shore, to his great dismay because anyone might have been observing them in their exposed situation. He raised her as quickly as he could, and then immediately she began to weep and to exclaim at the woeful state of his Royal Highness. Indeed, he did present a very sorry spectacle, for his beard was grown, his plaid hung in tatters, his eyes were swollen from the stings of the midges, and his legs and arms were covered in bruises and scratches, some new and some old.

" My lady," said he cheerfully, " I do assure you that I do very well, and it would not be amiss for all kings if they could pass through the same hardships as it has been my lot to undergo, for then they would understand the miseries and wrongs of the poorest of their subjects."

" It is a marvellous thing to me," murmured Lady Clanranald, wiping her eyes, " that your Royal Highness has so far escaped capture."

" It is a marvellous thing indeed," answered Charles gravely, " that I am fallen among such people as you have here in the Highlands. There is thirty thousand pounds' reward upon my head, madam, and yet, though I have been wandering and hiding for more than two months among those who are so poor they can scarce get bread to eat, only one wretched boy has attempted to betray me, and even he, I am sure, did it without malice. Come now, let us go into the house, where the good people are preparing supper for us, and on our way thither, you must permit me to carry this bundle."

The bundle of which he spoke was under Lady Clanranald's arm, and was a bulky one, wrapped up in a blanket to keep it dry. My lady dried her eyes at mention of it (though she would by no means be persuaded to permit Charles to relieve her of it, saying that would be most unfitting for a prince), and told him in a pleased tone that it contained some clothes for him.

" There is a gown of flowered calico," said she brightly, " with a light-coloured quilted petticoat to wear beneath it, a cloak of dun camlet made after the Irish fashion with a hood, a linen snood, stout shoes and woollen stockings. I believe they will fit your Royal Highness right bravely, tall though you are."

Charles groaned to himself at this reminder that he must now disguise himself as a woman, but he would not offend Lady Clanranald by letting her see how dismayed he was at the prospect, after all she had done for him, so he thanked her, and turned the conversation.

The poor people of the house had prepared the best supper they could obtain; it consisted of the heart, liver, and kidneys of one of their few precious sheep, washed down by a drink known as bland, which was made from whey close-stoppered for a number of years until it turned into a kind of wine. They were all very hungry and very merry; the Militia had gone just in time, Flora MacDonald had kept her promise, and soon they would be able to leave the Long Isle which had proved so dangerous to the Prince, and try their fortunes on the Isle of Skye. So it was a very cheerful meal; the fir-candles, which were splinters of fir dug out of the bogs, spat and sparkled in their iron holders, the wind blowing in through the cracks in the turf-wall puffed at the peat-smoke and gently swayed the mutton hams which hung on the rafters, and the dogs snored peacefully on the fox-skins.

It was all so very warm and homely after that horrible hiding-place in the rock, and O'Neil, who had drunk rather a lot of bland, had just risen to his feet to propose a toast to Miss Flora, when there came the sound of running footsteps outside, the door burst open, and Neil MacKechan, who had been keeping watch, came dashing in to tell them that General Campbell had just landed on the Long Isle with fifteen hundred soldiers, that he had heard that Captain Ferguson was joining him with two thousand more, and that all were even now marching towards Lady Clanranald's house at Ormaclade, being certain that the Prince was in hiding there.

"I must return home without delay," said Lady Clanranald, rising in tremulous haste and reaching for her cloak. "The longer I can keep the red soldiers in talk at my house, the better chance will there be of your

Royal Highness making your escape. If you will row me over the loch, it is but a step from there to Ormaclade, and then your Royal Highness and Miss Flora may lie hidden on the shore with the boatmen until the darkness falls and you can set sail for Skye."

So, thanking the people of the house for their kindness and hospitality, and taking some of their unfinished supper with them in a bag, the whole party hastened down to the lochside and got into the boat. The wind was against them, and it was not until the early hours of the morning that they reached the other side of this sea-loch. There, having made a breakfast of the remains of their supper, Lady Clanranald prepared to depart.

" And you likewise," said Flora unexpectedly, addressing O'Neil, " must now be leaving us."

" Leaving you ? " gasped O'Neil. " But why ? "

" Because I cannot be taking you to Skye, Captain O'Neil," said Flora firmly. " I have a pass made out for one man-servant, and that is my own servant, Neil MacKechan here."

" But what is to be become of me ? " cried poor O'Neil.

" That I do not know," replied Flora indifferently. "You must fend for yourself, as hundreds of other fugitives are doing at this moment. Your presence with us would endanger his Royal Highness, and that should be enough to make you anxious to be out of his company."

O'Neil's face was a study as he heard this. He had been so convinced that Flora was in love with him, and had bragged about it so loudly to the Prince, that he did not know whether he was more hurt by her indifference to his welfare than despairing of what he must do to preserve his own safety.

" Nay, Miss," said Charles, who was very kind-hearted, " the captain is my friend, and has stuck by me most faithfully throughout my wanderings, and if you cannot bring him along with us, I must decline to go myself."

But at those words, Captain O'Neil was ashamed of himself, and, seizing the Prince's hand and laying it to his lips, he protested that he cared not what became of him if only he knew that his master was safe, declaring further that he was ready to take his chance of escaping on his own. His sudden manliness moved Lady Clanranald to offer him what assistance she could, and she told him that if he would accompany her on her way to Ormaclade, she would try to find one of her tenants who would care for him until the Militia had left this part of the Long Isle.

So Charles took farewell of this the last of his friends who had accompanied him from Culloden, and also of Lady Clanranald. They went off over the heather with many backward glances and wavings of the hand, and Charles, with Flora, MacKechan, and the boatmen prepared to make themselves as comfortable as possible until night came again and they could set out for Skye.

7

The Prince in Woman's Clothes

BUT meanwhile the Prince, it seemed, had a duty to perform, and no sooner had Lady Clanranald and Captain
O'Neil disappeared over the brae, than Flora reminded
him of it.

"It is now time," said she briskly, "for your Royal
Highness to become Betty Burke, my Irish spinster, and
therefore if you will please to take these garments, you
may make your disguise behind yonder rock. The rest
of us shall keep watch that no one comes near us without
warning."

Seeing that the moment he had dreaded was now
arrived, and that there was no help for it, Charles took
the bundle which Lady Clanranald had left with Flora,
and went off by himself to change. Having stripped
himself of his tattered plaid, he first put on the quilted
petticoat, which, to his surprise, fitted him quite well,
having long strings to tie round the waist. But when it
came to the gown, it was a different matter. First of all,
in his ignorance, he put it on back to front, and as
ladies' dresses had in those days a sort of bustle or gather-

ing at the back, he found that it looked very odd. It dawned upon him what had happened, so he endeavoured to get out of it again, but this was far more difficult than he had imagined, for it was very tight for him, and besides he was not used to managing skirts. In the terrific struggle he had to get it back over his head, the stitches under one armhole gave way with a noise like pistol shots; then, having wrestled and pulled and pushed himself into it the right way, he was quite unable to make it fasten at the back. At last, panting, and scarlet in the face, he called piteously to Flora, who was sitting in the heather near by :

"Miss, Miss ! if you cannot help me, I never shall be able to wear this gown."

Flora came at once, and taking hold of the hooks on one side and the eyes on the other, pulled them together with all her might.

"There are bones or something sticking into me," gasped Charles. "If you could wait until I rip them out——"

"Of course there are bones in the bodice," interrupted Flora impatiently, "as there are in every lady's dress. Your Royal Highness will get used to them. And if you will just keep quiet, I shall be able to manage the better."

With that, she pulled harder than ever, until Charles thought that he would surely burst.

"I cannot breathe ! " he spluttered. "It is no use, I shall have to wear the gown unfastened and trust to the cloak to hide it."

"You cannot wear your cloak in the house," said the practical Flora. "Your Royal Highness must hold your breath until I have fastened the hooks. Blessings on you, have you endured so much to be daunted by a lady's gown?"

Ruthlessly she fastened hook after hook, until Charles felt as though he were encased in a suit of armour.

"Now," said Flora, "your Royal Highness must shave off your beard, or very odd you will look in woman's clothes. Lady Clanranald brought a razor with the clothes, and you can use the water in yonder burn for a mirror, as do all the men up here."

Shaving in cold water, without soap and with a mirror which kept rippling about, was just about as difficult as putting on the gown, but the Prince managed it somehow, and Flora, when she had put the linen snood on his head, tying it under his chin, had tied an apron round his waist, and had made him change his shoes and stockings, surveyed him with some satisfaction; until she noticed an odd bulge in the pocket of his gown.

"I have put one of my pistols in my pocket," Charles told her, noticing her glance, "that if we are surprised by the enemy I can make some sort of a fight for it."

"Mercy upon me!" cried Flora. "What would they think, if they went about to search my Irish maid and found a pistol in her pocket? Your Royal Highness must take it out at once."

"Then I shall carry a thick stick with me," said Charles,

obeying her with some reluctance, " for I am determined not to be taken without a fight."

" If you remember to act the part of a woman, and not to speak unless it is absolutely necessary and then in a borrowed voice, you will not be taken at all," Flora told him briskly. " And now, let me put on your cloak and hood and then you will be ready. Hereafter I shall address you as ' Betty ', that you may become accustomed to your new character."

After this they rejoined the boatmen on the shore, and as it was very cold, they made a fire there, and all sat round it, waiting for the night. Charles made such jokes about his disguise, and put on such mincing airs and such a high-pitched voice that he soon had them all laughing heartily; until suddenly the faithful MacKechan, who as usual was on watch, signalled to them violently from his post to put out the fire and hide in the heather. One of the boatmen instantly raced down to the boat and bringing the baling-pan full of water flung it on the fire, while the others ran as hard as they could up the shore (poor Charles tripping and stumbling in his petticoats), and flung themselves down in the tall heath. Here they were joined by MacKechan, who, pointing silently down the loch, showed them that his warning had come not a moment too soon.

For there, just coming round a bend, were three boats full of the Militia. They rowed slowly, and evidently were patrolling the loch; the watery sun gleamed on their muskets and sword-hilts, and in each boat one man stood with a spy-glass to his eye, searching the surrounding country for fugitives.

" Our boat will betray our presence here," whispered Charles. " Seeing it drawn up on the shore, they will land and make a search."

" Your Royal Highness is right enough there," replied MacKechan in an undertone. " But before they will have seen it, I shall go down into it, and pretend to be at fishing."

Not waiting to discover whether his companions approved his suggestion or not, he rose and ran down to the shore again, pushed the boat out into the water, and, clambering into it, pretended to be busy with preparations for an evening's fishing. The Prince and Flora, with the boatmen, peeping through the heather, watched in great anxiety as the militia-boats came rowing up the loch in the direction of MacKechan. When they were near enough to hail him, a man in one of them shouted out to him in the Gaelic, evidently asking who he was and whether he had seen any fugitives. Mac-Kechan acted his part admirably; he shook his head, shrugged his shoulders, and assumed the air of a man ready enough for conversation and gossip. This had its effect, and after a few minutes the militia-boats continued their slow progress up the loch, the men with the spy-glasses still narrowly scanning the shores, but most fortunately missing the fugitives because of the height of the heather and bracken in which they lay concealed.

It was a very clear, fine evening when at last they set sail for Skye, but Charles, who by this time had learnt to understand the Gaelic tolerably well, heard one of the boatmen say to his companions that there would be foul weather before morning. Sure enough, scarcely had they sailed a league than the sea became rough and then very tempestuous. The boatmen began to shake their heads and to say that they would never make Skye in such weather, and Flora herself was so agitated and distressed by the thought that she had put the Prince into this danger, though through no fault of her own, that Charles, to keep up the spirits of the little company, started to sing some Highland songs. His throat was still very sore and it hurt him to sing, but he was a great believer in the power of a good rousing song in time of anxiety. He chose the songs composed by the Highland bards or poets on his coming over to them, and presently they were all joining in. There was one song of which they were particularly fond, called *An Incitement to the Gaels*, and it began like this :

" O Clans of the Gaels, who ever were loyal,
        Horo, make ready to go ;
And give service now, faithful to Charles,
        Horo, make ready to go.
Serve him each one without any delay,
Read not your danger, but in Christ put your trust ;
Proudly and noisily, well-equipped, stormily,
Eager to go with him, ardent and valorous,
        Horo, make ready to go ! "

It sounded much better in the Gaelic, but this was rather beyond Charles at the moment, and even in English it was such a rousing, rampaging song that very soon the boatmen had forgotten the weather and were rowing and singing with great good cheer.

Presently Flora, who was sitting in the bottom of the boat, fell asleep. It was dark now, and Charles, fearful that one of the boatmen might step on her while doing something to the boat, leaned above her and spread his hands over her head for her protection. During the night the wind dropped and they made greater speed, but with the morning came a thick fog, so that the men dared not row any longer lest they be driven upon the coast. So they continued drifting all morning, imprisoned in a little world of mist, having no compass and not knowing where they were. At about one o'clock, the fog suddenly lifted, and then they found themselves close inshore; so close that they could see that there was a guard-house on the cliff, and a number of the Militia patrolling the beach.

The Militia saw them at the same time, and immediately an officer among them shouted out to them to bring the boat to land.

"Pull as hard as you can out to sea again," cried Charles, but the men needed no telling; they were already bending furiously to their oars.

"Creator!" muttered MacKechan. "They have three boats there. Fear is on me that they will pursue us."

He had scarcely said this when a volley of shots came

whistling over their heads, as the Militia, seeing them pull out for the open sea, fired on them at the command of their officer.

" Pull hard ! " cried Charles to the boatmen.   " Don't fear the villains, for we shall beat them yet."

" We have no fear for ourselves whatever," replied one of the men, " if the Great Being will preserve your Royal Highness."

" I have a firm trust in God," replied Charles cheerfully, " for He has preserved me in a most marvellous manner so far on my wanderings, and I am resolved to keep my faith to the end."

When they had pulled out of range of the muskets, they altered course, and steered round a point out of sight of the Militia, who for some reason or other had not pursued them in their boats.

" Now God be thanked," said Flora, speaking for the first time since this peril had come upon them, " we are now come to the country of my own clan, the Mac-Donalds.   It is true that Sir Alexander MacDonald, the lord of these parts, is in the service of German George, but sure I am that your Royal Highness has nothing to fear from any of my name, now that you have no army at your back."

" I know it," answered Charles, " and therefore am resolved to land here and take my hazard on shore, for I believe the Militia at some time or other will be after us in their boats.   This is the Isle of Skye, and since I set out to try my fortunes here, it would be cowardly to sail away again just because, on my first coming, I chanced to encounter the Militia."

"We are come into Mougstat Bay," said Flora, shading her eyes with her hand and surveying the surrounding country, "and are very close to Mougstat House, the residence of Sir Alexander. I know he is away from home at this time, and as his wife, Lady Margaret, is loyal to your Royal Highness, the best thing I can do is to hasten to her and seek her help, while you and the boatmen hide on the shore."

This was agreed upon, and, taking Neil MacKechan with her so that he might act as messenger if she needed to communicate with the Prince during her absence, she hastened to Mougstat House.

To her dismay, she found it to be full of guests; worse still, she observed that some of them wore the red cross of the Militia in their bonnets. Lady Margaret welcomed her kindly, and Flora explained that she was on her way home to her mother's house; but she did not see how she was going to tell Lady Margaret the real purpose of her visit, since her hostess was surrounded with visitors. Presently, however, Flora saw an old friend among them. This was MacDonald of Kingsburgh, Sir Alexander's factor, an old gentleman with long white hair and moustaches. Flora knew him to be a staunch adherent of the Prince, and so, taking him aside, she whispered to him that she had something of the greatest importance to confide to him and Lady Margaret, and since it would be easy for him to obtain a private talk with their hostess, because he had only to say that he wished to speak to her on business connected with the estate, Flora begged him to arrange for the three of them to have a talk in my lady's little withdrawing-room.

But when they were come there, and Flora had told them that the Prince was close by and desperately in need of help, Lady Margaret threw up her hands in horror, and cried out that she and her family would be ruined if he remained in the neighbourhood; her husband being in the service of German George, he would be hanged as a traitor if he aided Charles, and as for entertaining the Prince, Flora could see for herself that the house was full of Militia officers.

" Then I know not what I must do," sighed Flora. " I dare not venture as far as my mother's house, because, though I have a pass, I do not believe it will be a very great protection, for his Royal Highness wears his disguise so ill, that if they went about to question us, I am sure they would see that he was not a woman at all, despite his petticoats. And," she added, the tears coming into her eyes, " he is so much in need of proper food and rest, that it is not to be thought of that he should stay skulking in the heather."

" Wait you now," interposed Kingsburgh. " That is very true what you say, my lady, that you cannot be putting your husband and your children in peril by entertaining his Royal Highness. But I am an old man; death cannot be far distant from me, and it is a small matter to me whether I am hanged or die in my bed. Therefore will I take his Royal Highness into my own house, at least for this night."

Both Lady Margaret and Flora were overjoyed by this solution to their several problems; and after some discussion it was decided that from Kingsburgh House, Charles should be conducted to the port called Portree upon the east side of Skye, and from there should cross to the little island of Raasay, which lay between Skye and the mainland. For the owner of Raasay, MacLeod, was a zealous Jacobite and had fought for the Prince at Culloden. So Neil MacKechan was sent down to the shore to tell the Prince that Kingsburgh was on his way to conduct him to his house, and Flora herself slipped out to a doctor's house in the neighbourhood, where there was staying a certain young Donald Roy, one of the Prince's officers who had been badly wounded at Culloden, and who, Lady Margaret was sure, would undertake to go to Raasay and let MacLeod know their plans.

As soon as he could leave Mougstat House without arousing suspicion, old Kingsburgh went quietly out by the back way, taking with him a bottle of Burgundy, a glass, and some bread and cold meat. Hastening down to the shore, he was startled to see rise up from the heather in front of him a most ungainly figure. It was dressed in a woman's gown and mantle, but it did not look at all like any woman he had ever seen; its skirts were held up round its knees, its stockings had slipped down to expose hairy legs, and it was brandishing a great thick cudgel. Advancing upon Kingsburgh, it called out in a high, squeaky voice :

" Who are you ? "

Kingsburgh, who knew it must be the Prince, had hard work to conceal his amusement, for Charles was certainly a most comical sight, especially as, in brandishing the cudgel, he had just burst the fastenings of his gown and was trying frantically to do them up again. But then emotion overcame all Kingsburgh's desire to laugh, and it was as much as he could do not to kneel and seize the Prince's hand. Instead, he made a small bow, told the Prince who he was, and showed him the provisions he had brought with him. Charles was impatient to be on his way, but consented to eat and drink a little; immediately afterwards, bidding the boat-men return to the Long Isle, since their services were no longer required, Charles and his new guide set out on foot for Kingsburgh House.

It was a long walk, and a very uncomfortable one, both for the Prince and his friend. For Charles had the greatest possible difficulty in remembering that he was supposed to be a woman; he strode along at his usual rapid pace, and finding his petticoats unmanageable, kept hitching them up round his knees, especially when they had to cross one of the innumerable burns. Besides this, he would talk in what he supposed was a woman's voice, but which was, in fact, a quite unnatural sort of squeak. Kingsburgh saw how right Miss Flora had

Its stockings had slipped down to expose hairy legs and
it was brandishing a great thick cudgel.

been when she had said that the disguise was an ill one; he begged Charles to conduct himself more modestly while he was obliged to wear it, and also not to speak unless it was absolutely necessary. The Prince received the rebuke in good part, and the next time they had to cross a burn, he let his petticoats trail in the water.

Presently they heard hoof-beats behind them, and looking round, saw Miss Flora, escorted by MacKechan and a maid-servant lent her by Lady Margaret. Flora was riding pillion with the maid, and neither she nor MacKechan took any notice of the two foot travellers, beyond making them a little salute as they passed by. But the maid was very interested in Charles; she kept staring back at him, and could be heard saying to Flora what a curious looking woman that was, what long strides she took, and how awkwardly she managed her petticoats.

" Creator ! " she exclaimed innocently. " She is more like a man than any woman I ever saw."

It was night when they reached Kingsburgh House; they found that Flora and her escort had just arrived, but that Kingsburgh's wife, Mrs MacDonald, was already in bed, and had sent down a message to Flora to make her excuses, since she was very tired.

" That will not do at all," said Kingsburgh, when he heard this. " The goodwife must come down and provide us with supper, as we cannot be having the servants in."

So up he went to his wife's bedchamber, and telling her that they had another guest besides Miss Flora, insisted that she came down to attend to their needs.

When Mrs MacDonald came into the hall, she saw what she took to be a very tall, ungainly looking female seated in a chair. The female rose at once, came up to her, and, in the custom of those days, kissed her on both cheeks. The Prince's beard was beginning to grow again, and feeling bristles on the face which thus saluted her, Mrs MacDonald gave a gasp of fear and astonishment, drew her husband into another room, and in trembling accents asked him whether their visitor was one of those unfortunate gentlemen who were fugitives from the Battle of Culloden.

" He is that," replied Kingsburgh gravely.

" Does he bring any news of our poor Prince ? " asked his wife.

Kingsburgh took her hands and held them firmly.

" My dear," said he, " he is the Prince himself."

" Oh my grief ! " cried Mrs MacDonald, snatching her hands away and flinging her apron over her face, " now we shall all be hanged."

" Never you mind about that," responded her husband, patting her shoulder. " We can die but once, and if we are hanged for this, we shall die in a good cause. But if we conduct ourselves discreetly, we shall live yet, and have the comfort of having aided his Royal Highness. Now do you send up some supper. Fetch what is readiest; you have eggs, butter, and cheese in the house; get them as quickly as you are able."

" Eggs, butter, and cheese ! " echoed his wife shrilly. " What a supper is that for a prince ! "

"Oh, goodwife," replied Kingsburgh gently, "little do you know how this good Prince has been living for some time past. These, I can assure you, will be a feast for him. Besides, it would be unwise to be dressing a formal supper, because this would serve to raise the curiosity of the servants. The less ceremony and work the better. Make haste; and see that you come to supper with us."

"I come to supper?" repeated his wife in dismay. "How can I come? I know not how to behave in the presence of princes."

"You must come," insisted Kingsburgh, "for he will not eat a bit until he sees you at the board. And you will find it no difficult matter to behave before him, so obliging and easy is he in his conversation."

So Mrs MacDonald, still very flustered and embarrassed, brought up the simple supper; and soon she found it was as her husband had said, the Prince was so natural and easy that in five minutes he had her talking and laughing as though she had known him all her life. He ate four eggs and plenty of bread and cheese, washing it down with two bottles of beer. Afterwards, when the ladies had left the room, he and Kingsburgh sat by the fire with brandy and tobacco, and the Prince entertained his host with the tale of his past adventures. It was such a thrilling story that they stayed up till one o'clock in the morning, at which hour Kingsburgh took the Prince upstairs and showed him where he was to sleep. Charles exclaimed in delight at the four-post bed and the clean sheets, saying he had not slept in such luxury since his defeat at Culloden. He stripped off his petticoats, leapt into bed, and was asleep before Kingsburgh had finished saying good-night.

When Kingsburgh came to wake him next morning, he found him sleeping so soundly that he had not the heart to disturb him, though he knew that he ought to be on his way to Portree. At last, at one o'clock, he came in again, and found Charles newly awakened and looking much refreshed. As they were talking, there was a shy knock upon the door, and Mrs MacDonald and Flora came hesitantly into the room. They were whispering together, and Flora was blushing, so Charles asked them what was amiss.

" Mistress MacDonald here," replied Flora, smiling shyly, " has been begging me to get a lock of your Royal Highness's hair as a memento of your visit, but I did not like to ask such a favour."

" Why, Miss," cried Charles reproachfully, " is that so great a favour to ask of me, who owe you my life ? Pray sit down on this chair by the bed, and you may cut off as much of my hair as you please."

So Flora sat down by the bedside, and he laid his head in her lap; she cut off a lock of his long fair hair, and, dividing it into two, gave Mrs MacDonald the one half and kept the other for herself. Then she said that it was time the Prince was dressed, and begged leave for herself and her hostess to assist him in putting on his female garments, because he must leave the house as he

123

had come, otherwise any of the servants who had seen him last night, might wonder and begin to talk. He groaned a little at having to put on those wretched petticoats again, but soon he had them all laughing so much that the tears ran down their cheeks; he minced about the room, taking little short steps, put on his high, squeaky voice, and asked them did they think this gown became him? When he was dressed he cried to Flora in the same tone :

"Oh, Miss, you have forgot my apron. Now where, pray, is my apron? Please to get me my apron here, for it is such a pretty one, and when I am at my spinning, it serves to keep me clean."

When at last he had been tied and pinned into his clothes (for all the fastenings were broken), he took a kindly farewell of Mrs MacDonald, and, with Kingsburgh and Neil MacKechan, set out towards Portree, Flora and the maid going on horseback by another route. When they were a safe distance from the house, Kingsburgh produced from under his plaid a complete Highland gentleman's dress, and going into some whin-bushes by the side of the track, Charles changed into these. There was a tartan waistcoat, a little-plaid or kilt, a coat of deer-hide, tartan stockings, a blue bonnet, and Highland brogues. Kingsburgh showed him how to prick holes in the brogues with his dirk, so that when he had to ford a river the water might run out of them. He gave Charles also a sporran with some money in it, and a new dirk to wear in his stocking. Then they hid the female garments in a bush, for Kingsburgh to collect when it was dark.

Up till now, the Prince had maintained his high spirits, but at the necessity to part from Kingsburgh, who had been so kind to him, he could not keep up the pretence of cheerfulness, and he was so distressed that, to Kingsburgh's dismay, blood began pouring from his nose.

"It is nothing at all," said Charles, mopping at his streaming nose. "This bleeding is only the effect of parting from a dear friend, and often happens to me in such a case. I believe it is a very common accident among members of my family. Alas, Kingsburgh, I am afraid I shall not meet with another MacDonald in my wanderings, and though other clans have proved loyal to me, your own is the one I trust more than all the rest."

"Your Royal Highness may count upon the fidelity of MacLeod of Raasay," replied Kingsburgh, trying to cheer both the Prince and himself. "For though the MacLeods as a clan did not rise for you, there are many of that name fought in your army, and wish you well."

"I know it," said Charles, "and can never forget my good, honest Donald MacLeod who led me for so long a way upon my flight. Yet the name MacDonald will ever remain dearest to my heart."

So they parted, and Charles was guided by Neil Mac-Kechan to a change-house at Portree, where he found Flora awaiting him. They lay there that night, and next day, which was the 1st of July, Donald Roy visited them with the news that MacLeod was sending his boat later that same day to convey the Prince to Raasay. Since Flora's part in his adventures was now finished, she bade him good-bye and prepared to set out for her mother's house, attended by MacKechan and the maid. She wept a great deal at parting; the Prince took her hands and kissed them as reverently as if she had been a queen, as he said earnestly :

" For all that has happened, Miss Flora, I hope that we shall yet meet at my father's palace in London, when he is restored to his own, and that there I may have the honour of another dance with you."

8

The Ghostly Journey

THE Prince spent two days on the little island of Raasay, living in a low, mean hut with a leaky roof. He was quite used to discomforts of all kinds by this time, yet never had he felt so depressed as during these two days.

For one thing, he was sad at parting from Flora, whose practical good sense and salty humour had been a great tonic to him; and for another, though he knew that the men who now had charge of his safety were good and loyal, he knew also that their clan had not risen for him, and therefore he had to be very careful what he said to them, for it was a sore subject with them, and like all their race they were very quick to take offence. MacLeod of Raasay himself, the chief of this sept of the clan, was not on the island at present, and it was his son, known as Young Raasay, with his brother Murdoch, and his second cousin, Captain Malcolm MacLeod, who had gone over to Skye to fetch Charles over. Young Raasay was a gloomy man, who hastened to give the Prince all the bad news he could think of; Murdoch was a fierce-looking person who was fond of taking out his dirk and sharpening it as though longing to stick it into somebody; and Captain Malcolm was a silent individual and had a nervous air.

After informing Charles that most of the men who had aided him so far in his adventures had been captured, including old Donald MacLeod, Ned Burke, Captain O'Neil, and MacDonald of Kingsburgh, Young Raasay went on to say that there was at present on the island a stranger who had come to sell tobacco, but that now when his tobacco was all sold, he was still lingering here, so in all probability he was a spy. Scarcely had Young Raasay finished telling Charles this, than, through the open doorway of the hut, they saw a man approaching them across the moor, and Young Raasay, with a low exclamation of alarm, whispered that this was none other than the stranger in question.

" Then we must lie quiet," said Charles, " and trust that he will not come into the hut."

" Better to make sure that he will not return again," said Murdoch; and to the Prince's horror, he seized his gun and took aim at the approaching figure.

" Oh no ! " cried Charles in dismay, catching Murdoch's arm. " God forbid that any poor man should suffer for me, if I can but keep myself anyways safe. For all we know, he may be harmless, and in any case, Murdoch, I will not have bloodshed on my account."

Murdoch was rather angry about this, and muttered under his breath; it was obvious that he thought the

Prince very soft, though of course he could not say so. Fortunately for them all, the stranger passed by the hut without looking into it, and went on his way. The incident, however, had convinced Charles that he ought to get off this small island as soon as possible, and he urged his companions to take him back to Skye. He knew it was full of the Militia, and that since Kingsburgh had been captured so soon after aiding him the hunt there must be very hot; yet he felt he would be safer in the larger island, for though the MacDonald country was closed to him, there was MacKinnon country in the south of Skye, and this clan was very loyal.

So that very evening they crossed the narrow strip of water in a small boat, and after a very stormy voyage they landed at ten o'clock at night near Scorobeck on the north coast of Skye. Hauling up the boat and concealing it among some rocks, they set out to find shelter, for it was pouring with rain and they were all soaked through. After walking some two miles, they spied a cow-byre; Young Raasay thought it would not be safe to enter it in case there was a herdsman there, but Charles was so miserable at this time that he felt reckless, and cared for nothing but to get out of the rain. There was nobody in the byre, and after they had eaten some bread and cheese which they had brought with them, the Prince lay down to sleep while the others kept watch. He could not sleep for a long while, he was so depressed and restless, and when at last he did, his companions observed how, even in his sleep, he tossed and turned, threw himself about on the ground, and sometimes started up, crying out in a most anguished voice :

" Oh poor Scotland ! Oh poor Scotland ! "

When morning dawned, he begged Young Raasay and Murdoch to part from him and return to their home, pretending that he would be safer with only one companion, but the truth of it was their company depressed him, and he felt that if Young Raasay told him any more bad news, or if Murdoch sharpened his dirk once more, he might forget his manners and be rude to them. So after much hesitation they left him, in the care of Captain Malcolm MacLeod.

During the afternoon, Charles had a more restful sleep, and when he awoke he felt better. Looking round for his companion, he observed him sitting in the doorway of the byre, gazing fixedly and with a deep frown at the lochan on the shores of which the byre was situated. As it seemed obvious that there was some danger present, Charles crept to Malcolm's side, and asked in a whisper :

" Is it the Militia ? "

Malcolm shook his head, but went on staring and frowning. Charles followed the direction of his eyes, but all he could see was the cold, dark water of the lochan, with trout leaping in it, and tall reeds edging its banks.

" I am not liking this place at all," muttered Malcolm presently, " for it was here my grandfather caught the water-horse, which was a woeful day for him whatever."

Charles looked at him to see if he was serious; it was plain that he was, so the Prince asked him, smiling :

" Are there really such things as water-horses, Malcolm ? "

The question seemed to affront his companion.

" Indeed and there are," said he. " Am I not telling you that my grandfather caught one in this very lochan, which he did by putting the cow-shackle round its neck, for like all fairy things it can be tamed by cold iron. And then he took it home and employed it with the mortal horses in carting of peat, but one fine day it slipped the cow-shackle and off it went into the loch, dragging the mortal horses along with it (they being all tied nose to tail). And when it had got them down into its watery haunts, it devoured them, every bit of them except the livers, which it will not eat whatever."

" Well," said Charles, trying to cheer them both up (for Malcolm's story had been told with such gravity that the Prince almost believed it, especially in this lonely place), " if the water-horse is dangerous only to mortal horses, we are safe. But I think, Malcolm, that we should be getting on our way, for it is my purpose to walk all night."

" Walk at night ? " cried Malcolm in dismay. " Your Royal Highness cannot be doing any such thing, especially on this day of the week."

" It is safer during the darkness," replied Charles. " And I do not see why a Friday should be——"

" Hush you ! Hush you ! " interrupted Malcolm in great agitation. " It is most unlucky to call that day by its name; you must call it instead the Day of Yonder

Town. For it is the day of the People of Peace, what you would be at calling the fairies, and upon this day of the week they have especial power over mortals; nothing must be done to offend them—a blessing be on their journeying and travelling," he added, glancing over his shoulder and smiling ingratiatingly at something invisible. " As for walking at night," he went on, " it is the most dangerous of all things, for they are then at their most malevolent, and love to lead the traveller astray."

Charles longed to say that he cared nothing for the People of Peace if only he did not meet the Militia, but seeing that Malcolm was exceedingly superstitious and took the matter of the fairies very seriously, he appealed to him instead to brave the dangers of the night for his Prince's sake, pointing out to him that he himself had no one now but Malcolm on whom to rely. The appeal was successful, Malcolm saying stoutly that he would brave the Devil himself (whom he called the Son of Cursing or the Big Mischief), if only he might be of service to his Prince. So they set out. Malcolm insisted that Charles carry his dirk in his hand, cold iron being some protection against the fairies, but he lamented that they could not carry also a handful of oatmeal well sprinkled with salt, for this was the traditional protection on ' the Day of Yonder Town '.

After they had been walking some distance, Malcolm halted, and said in a more practical tone :

" Your Royal Highness will pardon me to ask where

you are going, for that I dread you may chance to fall into the hands of the Militia, if you do not take exceeding good care, as there are many small parties dispersed up and down Skye."

" Why, Malcolm," replied Charles wearily, " I now throw myself entirely into your hands, and leave you to do with me what you please. Only I want to go into the MacKinnons' country. I hope you will accompany me, if you can lead me safely thither."

" I can do that," replied his companion, " but I must tell you that we have a long journey to make, no less than thirty miles, for I dare not lead you by the direct route, but take you by-ways, and go here and there across the island to keep as free as we can of the parties scattered up and down."

" I have grown used to long walks," answered the Prince, " and you will not hear me complaining of fatigue."

" There being still so little darkness at this time of the year," said Malcolm, " we may very easily be spied by someone, and therefore you will excuse me if I suggest that your Royal Highness passes as my servant, and makes such changes in your dress and manner as may fit the character."

So Charles took off the tartan waistcoat which Kingsburgh had given him and exchanged it for Malcolm's plain one; he ripped the buckles from his shoes and the ruffles from his shirt, took off his bonnet and wrapped his head up in a dirty napkin, drawing it about his face

133

as though he had the toothache. Having done all this, he said cheerfully to Malcolm :

" I think I will now pass well enough for your servant, and I will borrow the name of Lewie Caw, who was a young surgeon lad in my army. Look at me, Malcolm, and tell me what you think. How will it do ? "

" Not very good whatever," replied Malcolm frankly. " For those who have seen your Royal Highness before would still know your face for all the disguise you are in."

" This," said Charles, laughing, " is an odd remarkable face I have got that nothing can disguise it."

" There is not a person," replied Malcolm solemnly, " that knows the air of a great and noble man, but upon seeing your Royal Highness in any disguise you could put on, would not see somewhat about you that is out of the ordinary, something of the stately and the grand. Ach, but there is no help for that. You must take care to walk some little distance behind me, as befits my servant, you must carry the baggage, and if we meet with anyone known to me, you must not speak, but stand apart and take no notice whatever."

All these directions Charles promised to follow, and so they set out on their thirty mile walk. They travelled through glens and wild moors, all eerie and dim in the pale Highland night, meeting no one, and hearing only the burbling of streams, the sough of the wind, and the melancholy cry of some night-bird. Once Charles fell into a bog, going down to his waist, and it was only with great difficulty that Malcolm pulled him out again. The way was made longer because Malcolm insisted on avoiding not only the tracks but places where he felt himself to be in particular danger from the supernatural beings in whom he so firmly believed. Especially did he avoid those numerous little knolls with which the country was full, and once when they were resting for a short space, Charles enquired the reason for this.

" Ach, they are fairy-burghs," replied Malcolm, glancing over his shoulder in that nervous way he had whenever he spoke of such things. " Beneath them live the People of Peace. My grandfather, who had what we call the two-sights, that is, he was able to see and hear what is not given to mortal eyes and ears as a rule, has heard them down there at their singing, and the rap-rap of their hammers while they work. Indeed, and he has smelt their barley-cakes toasting, and his sister, who was married with a man of the Glencoe MacDonalds, was beloved by one of their young men, who enticed her into his burgh, and she was never seen again whatever."

Charles did not really believe all this; still, it made him feel rather uncomfortable, alone in that wild country in the night-time. However, it took his mind off the human peril which had dogged his footsteps for so long, and so, whenever they sat down for a rest, he asked Malcolm to tell him some more of his stories.

Malcolm was full of them. This grandfather of his had seen, on the eve of a great battle, the fairy washer-woman down at the pool, washing the winding-sheets of those who would die next day; he had seen blood upon

his son's claymore before the boy had girded himself
with it to fight for Charles's father, and at that battle,
sure enough his son had been slain. Malcolm's second
cousin had killed a hind on a Friday, and as hinds were
fairy cows, the People had shot their elf-bolts at him, and
had made the carcase so heavy with their spells that
neither man nor beast could carry it. There were other
supernatural beings besides the People, said Malcolm;
there were glaistigs, who were the ghosts of people so
attached to the houses where they had lived during life
that when they died their spirits returned to haunt them.
They were quite harmless, except to lazy servants, whom
they would punish by putting dust in their food or up-
setting cogs of milk and water, and when they foresaw
misfortune coming to the house, they would make a
terrible wailing.

There were things called urisks, too; Malcolm's
grandfather had come upon one of these creatures, who
were the children of a mortal and a fairy, one day when
he was by himself on the mountain. It was sitting by a
stream and was engaged in keeping the water from falling
too fast over the precipice. Much more awful had been
the grandfather's experience when, venturing out after
dark on a Friday, he had heard the People's bagpipes, and
had felt a whole band of fairies go by him in a cloud,
without sound, like a sudden cold wind when the night
was still. And Malcolm's own sister, a silly woman
who was accustomed to scoff at the existence of the
People, on one occasion had narrowly escaped being

killed by a fairy dog, which she had mistaken for a stirk;
it was as large as that animal, dark green in colour, with
eyes like live coals and a speed on it like lightning. By
the time morning dawned, the Prince had forgotten all
about the Militia in his thankfulness at having escaped the
People of Peace.

But with the morning, Malcolm became brisk and
practical, though he did not forget, either the duties
demanded by his simple religion, or those imposed by his
superstition. He took off his bonnet to the rising sun,
and kneeling down in the heather, said a short prayer, or
as he described it, ' took God upon his lips '. Then,
looking sharply over his shoulder, he gave an exclamation of joy; he explained to Charles that he looked over
his shoulder every morning after his prayer, and that the
first thing he saw then would show him whether it was
going to be a lucky or an unlucky day. This morning he
had seen a heron, which was a good sign; to have seen a
snipe, or a foal with its back to him, or a snail crawling
on a bare stone, would have foretold an unlucky day.

Then he went on to say that they were come into the
country of the MacKinnons, showing Charles how close
they were to the sea on the south of Skye, and pointing
out below them a clachan, where, he said, he had a sister
who was married with a Captain John MacKinnon, who
had served in the Prince's army. Captain MacKinnon,
he added, was one of the Chief of the MacKinnons'
tacksmen or principal gentlemen of the clan. Malcolm
proposed that he should go down alone to his brother-

in-law's house and see if it were safe for them to rest there for a while; if it was, he would return for Charles.

He was not gone long, and when he came striding back, he looked very cheerful. His brother-in-law, he said, was not at home at present, but his sister had been delighted to see him, and had told him that none of the Militia was in the district so far as she knew, and that he would be very welcome to stay with her. Thinking it safer for everyone that she should remain in ignorance of Charles's real identity, he had told her that he had a servant with him, Lewie Caw, who was in as much danger from the Militia as he was himself, and therefore he hoped that she would give him hospitality.

Malcolm's sister, whose name was Mairi, was standing at her door to welcome them when they arrived, the Prince still walking behind his pretended master, and carrying their little baggage on his shoulder.

" Well, look at that now ! " exclaimed Mairi, who was a plump, cheerful woman with a very kind face. " What a state this poor lad is in whatever ! "

Charles, who was indeed a sorry sight since he had fallen into the bog, made her a low bow but kept silent. She led them into her house and showed them a meal she had prepared for them; there was salmon fresh-caught from the river, strong-ale, bannocks, and a dish called froth, which was a kind of thin whipped cream made of stiffly beaten whey. A sulky looking servant lass was setting wooden platters and horn mugs on the table. Charles was very hungry after his long walk, but he remembered who he was supposed to be, and so he sat down at some distance from Malcolm and their hostess, and waited to be served last of all.

" You must come to the table and be at eating, Lewie," said Malcolm, observing this.

" Sir, I know my manners better than to do that," replied Charles humbly. " I do very well where I am."

" Certainly he must sit down with us," insisted Mairi, adding in an undertone to her brother : " I am not knowing what it is, but there is somewhat about that lad I find most gracious and charming; he does not look like a servant whatever."

After they had eaten and the servant lass was clearing the dishes, Malcolm suddenly asked her if she would bring some water and wash his feet, because he was so very much fatigued. The girl complied, though with no very good grace, and when she had finished, Malcolm said to her in Gaelic (for she had not a word of English) :

" You see that poor lad there. I hope you will wash his feet too, for he has as much need as I, and it would be a great charity."

The girl tossed her head angrily and cried :

" No such thing. Although I wash the master's feet, I am not obliged to wash the servant's. My grief, he's but a low countryman's son. I will not wash his feet whatever."

" Are you telling me that ? " cried Mairi, who had taken a great fancy to the supposed Lewie Caw. " Now the burning of your heart towards you, have you forgot your manners altogether? Did not the Blessed One Himself wash the feet of His poor disciples, and who are you, pray, to refuse a stranger the same courtesy? Give me the bowl; I will perform this service myself, for no guest of mine, be he rich or poor, shall have it to say that he did not find true hospitality in the house of a MacKinnon."

All this was extremely embarrassing for Charles, but he was obliged to let Mairi have her way, for he knew by now how very sacred to these Highlanders were the laws of hospitality to the stranger and the guest. Afterwards, Malcolm whispered to him that he should lie down and take some rest, while Malcolm himself went outside to keep guard lest any of the Militia passed that way after all.

He had not been there long before he saw a man come striding down the mountain side, and while he was yet some distance off, Malcolm recognised him by his flaming red hair and beard as his brother-in-law, Captain John MacKinnon. He rose and went to meet him; they grasped hands in greeting, and John explained to Malcolm that he had been up to see how the lads and lassies were getting along at the shieling-huts.

" And on my way down the ben," he added, " I was after seeing a sight which liked me not at all. For there in the sea are two ships of war belonging to German George. Bad luck to them! they are worse than the Militia."

"What," asked Malcolm slowly, "if our Prince be a prisoner on board one of them?"

"God forbid!" murmured John. "I would not wish that for anything."

"What then," continued Malcolm, glancing sideways at his brother-in-law, "if we had him here, John? Do you think he would be in safety enough?"

"I wish with all my heart we had him here," replied John fervently, "for I would count it the greatest honour to entertain his Royal Highness, and would give my life to preserve him."

"That's the good news that's in it whatever," replied Malcolm, "for I must tell you that he is here already. But," he went on earnestly, as John began to exclaim with wonder and delight, "when you go in you must take no notice of him at all. He passes as my servant, Lewie Caw, and your wife knows nothing of the business."

John promised to observe this behaviour, but when he entered his house and saw the Prince, who was sitting on the fail-sunk or earthern seat by the fire, the good Mac-Kinnon had hard work to restrain his emotion. Presently, when Mairi went to attend to some household duties, the brothers-in-law and Charles consulted as to what was to be done next. John MacKinnon was strongly of the opinion that the Prince should leave Skye, for it was known to the Militia that he had been upon the island recently, and a thorough search was even now in progress. He added that the best thing he could advise was for Charles to return to the mainland, because there the enemy had a much larger area to patrol, and so the chance of dodging the soldiers would be greater. Since this was the Prince's own opinion, he agreed, and John set off immediately to see about getting a boat.

He returned after half an hour or so to say that on his way to the shore he had met with his Chief, Old Mac-Kinnon, and he had taken the liberty of telling him of the Prince's whereabouts and plans. Charles was not very pleased about this, for he knew that Old MacKinnon was aged and infirm, and as he did not see how such a man could aid him, he thought it unwise of John to have disclosed his secret. However, he knew in what respect the clansmen held their chiefs, and how they went to them in every difficulty and trouble, so he said nothing, and waited for Old MacKinnon, who, said John, was now on his way to see his Royal Highness.

Presently there entered the house a very tall old gentleman, dressed finely in the Highland garb. He was in the trews, which were tight trousers of tartan covering him from waist to feet; a doe-skin jacket with large silver buttons clothed the upper part of his body, and in his blue bonnet was an eagle's feather, an ornament worn only by chiefs. Buckled round his waist was his broadsword with its hilt of silver; there was a pair of pistols stuck into his belt, and his dirk was tucked into a special pocket contrived for it under his armpit. With great ceremony he doffed his bonnet to Charles, and shook hands with him and then with Malcolm and John, though he had seen John only a few minutes earlier.

"The blessing of the Trinity be upon you, Sir," said he to the Prince. "I bid you welcome to my land and make you free of all I have. It grieves me that I cannot offer you the hospitality which is fitting, but that is not my blame. The best thing I can do for you at present is to transport you away from Skye as soon as may be, and for this purpose I have a boat in readiness on the shore, with four of my gillies to row it. We shall start, by your leave, when the sun sets, and meanwhile you will be permitting me to offer you some refreshment."

So saying, he produced a bottle of French wine and some fine biscuit, which, he said, had been sent him by his son who was in France. It was plain that the old man had taken upon himself the sole management of the Prince's present movements, and he had such an air of authority that when he said that Malcolm must not go with them, but must return to his home or otherwise he would be missed and a search made for him, Charles, though he had taken a great liking to Malcolm and would have wished for more of his company, fairies or no fairies, did not try to argue the matter.

They sat drinking and talking, and playing a hand at cards, until the sun set, when, saying good-bye to Malcolm MacLeod, the Prince went down to the boat, accompanied by Old MacKinnon, and his clansman, Captain John. Rowing all night, they reached the mainland in the early hours of the morning. It was the 5th of July, and Charles had been hiding in the islands just ten weeks.

9

The Chase in the Loch

THEY landed at a place called Little Mallaig on the shores of Loch Nevis, and Old MacKinnon set out at once to find some secure refuge for the Prince, who, he said, must remain here until his return. As the weather had turned suddenly fine and hot, Charles, with John MacKinnon and the four boatmen, camped in the open air by the loch-side, and here they stayed for three nights.

They dared not light a fire, in case there were soldiers in the neighbourhood, but they were able to cook the trout they caught on hot stones, so strong was the sun at mid-day. It was a peaceful place and very beautiful; the banks of the loch were bright with yellow flags, meadow-sweet, clover and ragged-robins, and through its clear waters could be seen a forest of tangle-weed in which small fish darted to and fro. It was good to feel warm again, and dry, after so much cold and rain; the only real discomfort was caused by the clegs, for this was the worst month for them, and their bites were terrible. They saw not a sign of the soldiers, but on the third morning, very early, the Prince was awakened by John MacKinnon, who told him in a whisper that during the night some gipsies had camped in their neighbourhood, and that he did not like it at all.

"For there is no trusting that sort of people whatever," said he. "They will stick by one another to the death, but will not scruple to rob and betray other men if they think there is money in it; likewise are they very inquisitive, and it will not be long before we shall have them round us if we stay here, enquiring who we are."

He added that in his opinion they should take the boat and row up the loch, leaving one of the boatmen behind in order to meet Old MacKinnon on his return and tell him what had happened. Charles did not like this proposal, for they had nowhere to go, and besides, it might offend Old MacKinnon. However, John was now in charge of him, so he thought it best to do as he said.

When they had got into the boat, John took the tiller, and asked the Prince to sit down as low as he could and rest his head between John's knees, in order that if they were seen by anybody, Charles would be concealed as much as possible. So they began to row steadily through the sweet pure air of the summer's morning across the still waters of the loch, which had scarcely a ripple to disturb it. All this coast was very thickly wooded, the trees and undergrowth coming right down to the shore. Also it was very winding and full of little bays and promontories, and here and there a tiny rocky islet stuck out of the water, on which some wild swans had their nests and seals basked in the sun. The sound of their oars alone disturbed the silence, and all around them the mountains dreamed in a blue mist.

Charles was almost asleep, lulled by the slow rhythm of the oars, when suddenly he heard John give a startled exclamation. He sat up and rubbed his eyes, and then he saw that, on rounding a promontory, they had come upon a row-boat tied to a rock, and were so close to it that their oars had touched its side. He had just time to see, gathered on the shore within fifty yards of them, five men with red crosses in their bonnets, before John thrust him down into the bottom of the boat again, and threw the ends of his plaid over the Prince's head.

" Ho there ! " cried a man's voice from the shore. " From whence do you come ? "

" From Sleat," John called back, as calmly as he could.

" Row ashore for examination," shouted the other voice.

" Pull for your lives, lads ! " muttered John to the oarsmen; and immediately the boat began to fly through the water.

" Are we pursued ? " asked Charles, his voice coming muffled through the folds of the plaid.

" They are after us in their boat," replied John. " My curse be upon them and upon all their race ! But we have a start and shall beat them yet."

" Let me take the spare oar and we shall go the faster," said the Prince, throwing aside the plaid and trying to sit

146

up. But John held him down with a hand on his shoulder.

" Your Royal Highness will lie quiet where you are," said he sharply. " You are in my charge, and must do as I say."

It was horrible to lie there without being able to see anything, but Charles could not bring himself to defy this good friend of his who was doing his best to assist him. Through the muffling folds of the plaid he could hear the sounds of pursuit drawing steadily nearer, the furious splash of oars and a babel of voices.

" There are four muskets in the bottom of the boat," said John to the oarsmen. " Have them ready to fire at my word. And then, my lads, be sure to take aim and mark well, and there is no fear."

" No, no, John ! " cried the Prince. " The sound of shots may bring the soldiers down on us, if there are any in the neighbourhood."

" I shall not give the order to fire," answered John shortly, " unless they come level with us, but if it comes to that, it is necessary that none of them survive to tell the tale."

The words had scarcely left his lips when the whine and bite of a bullet shattered the silence of the morning. It was deafening in that still air, awaking echoes in the hills; it was followed by another, and another, and each time the hiss of the bullet in the water seemed nearer than the last.

" Do not you be at returning their fire until I give the

word," cried John to the oarsmen, " but pull for your lives, boys. They cannot be busy with their muskets and their oars at the same time, and with luck we shall soon be out of range."

It was a race against death, and a very hot one. The Militia were firing almost continuously, their bullets peppering the water around the other boat, and one or two of them grazing the sides. Charles felt horribly useless and helpless, lying there not able to do a thing, and he did not see how they were ever going to escape. But then, peeping between the folds of the plaid, he saw John suddenly seize the spare oar, and at the same time heard him shout a direction to the rowers in Gaelic. Skimming rapidly round an out-thrust of land, they drove the boat under the overhanging branches of the trees, pushing these aside with their hands, so that in a moment they were completely concealed.

" Quick now," said John to the Prince, flinging aside the plaid, " you and I will be making a dash for it while these lads remain with the boat. If the Militia see them, they will not be daring to approach, lest they be fired upon from this concealment. If they come near, lads, let them see your muskets pointing through the branches."

Scrambling to his feet, Charles sprang out of the boat on to the slippery bank, and began worming his way in the track of John, who was going swiftly through the bushes and bracken. It was a most exhausting scramble. The branches scratched his face and hands and hooked themselves into his clothes, the uneven ground continually tripped him, and the pace John set made his heart thump in his breast and his body stream with sweat. From behind him he could hear the shouts of the Militia, but they had ceased firing, and evidently John had been right in saying that they would not dare approach too close to the concealed boat. So active was the Prince, and so used by now to escaping over rough ground, that John was not ten paces ahead of him when they gained the top of the hill and flung themselves, panting and exhausted, among the bracken.

From where they lay they could see the militia-boat pulling out from the shore again, and at this John told the Prince that he could take some rest. He was so tired that he slept for three hours, not even the clegs disturbing him, and it was only the heat of the sun which at last awakened him, for the place where he lay was without shade and it was now mid-day. He found John MacKinnon fidgeting to be off on some errand; there was an island in the loch not far from here, John told him, and as he had seen smoke coming from it, he knew it must be inhabited. He proposed, therefore, to row over and discover whether there was anyone there who could help them in their present situation. Meanwhile, Charles must stay here and lie concealed in the bracken.

After what seemed a long while, the Prince saw the flaming red head of John MacKinnon appearing and disappearing through the undergrowth below him, and in a few minutes his friend was sitting beside him once more. It was plain that John was very much put out about something; he muttered to himself in the Gaelic, and then burst out :

" Astonishment is upon me to have heard a gentleman like Old Clanranald talk at such a rate as he was doing to me just now. I think he must have been taken out of himself."

" Why," said the Prince, " is Old Clanranald on the island, then ? "

" He is," replied John. " He is in hiding there, and seems to think more of his own skin than of the safety of his Prince."

" He has suffered much in my cause already," said Charles quietly.

" And so has many a better man," retorted John. " Yet does that excuse any one of us, chief or clansman, from risking our lives and all that we have in securing your Royal Highness from your enemies ? Besides, he will not so much as advise us what we must do next, saying he knows not anywhere which is safe for your Royal Highness at this time."

" Well, John," said the Prince, shrugging his shoulders, " there is no help for it. We must do the best we can for ourselves."

" And that is to return whence we came," answered John, " where we may find my Chief, who, old as he is, will not desert your Royal Highness while there is breath in his body."

It was now evening, and although it was still quite light, the declining sun threw shadows of which the oarsmen took advantage, keeping close inshore on the other side from that on which they had encountered the militia-boat, and making ready to land upon any alarm. But they saw no one, and presently arrived back safely at Little Mallaig. Here they found Old MacKinnon pacing up and down in great agitation, not knowing what was become of them, and not liking to leave the place without news of them. He advised sending the boat back to Skye, and walking to Morar, some eight miles distant, where he hoped that MacDonald of Morar would give them hospitality and perhaps suggest some more permanent refuge. It was plain that the old Chief was very worried by the whole situation, but he did his best to cheer Charles by telling him stories of Morar's famous hospitality and comfortable house.

But when they arrived at their destination, they saw only a blackened ruin where this house had been; it had been burnt very recently, for a few thin skeins of smoke still wreathed about the timbers. They were gazing upon the scene in great dismay, when they were hailed in the Gaelic by a short, thick-set man, whose eagle's feather proclaimed him to be a chief. It was plain from his expression that he had recognised the Prince, but he was wise enough to give no greeting, only beckoned them to follow him. Old MacKinnon whispered to Charles that this was MacDonald of Morar. Their new friend guided them to a herdsman's bothie, and when he had ushered them inside, he kneeled and kissed the Prince's hand, begging him to excuse such poor hospitality, but it was all he had to offer, Captain Ferguson and his soldiers having fired his house only a few days previously.

Next day, Morar volunteered to go and seek for Young Clanranald, saying that he would be better minded to serve his Prince than his father had been, and they being here on the edge of Clanranald's estates on the mainland, the son of the Chief would be the best person to give advice and provide a refuge at this juncture. But in the evening he returned to say that he could not find Young Clanranald anywhere, and he added that there seemed to be a great number of the red soldiers in the neighbourhood. After some consultation, it was decided that in the evening, the Prince, Morar, and John MacKinnon should walk to the house of Angus MacDonald of Boradale, where, if the Prince should be no safer, at least he would be more comfortable. So they bade good-bye to Old MacKinnon, and set out, arriving in the early hours of the following morning at Boradale's house, only to find that it too had been burned to the ground, and that its owner, like Morar, was living in a wretched hut.

However, Boradale was overjoyed to see Charles, and promised that he and his two sons, Ranald and John, would undertake to provide the Prince with a refuge. Leaving him in such good hands, John MacKinnon and Morar took their leave.

"Now the best person to act as guide to your Royal

Highness in this country," said Boradale, when the others had departed, " is Glenaladale, a gentleman with whom methinks your Royal Highness is well acquainted."

" I am indeed," replied Charles eagerly. " Major MacDonald of Glenaladale was one of my favourite officers, and I would give much to see him again. But is he in this neighbourhood ? "

" I think he is that," answered Boradale. " I will send my son John to find him, and to ask him to come hither at once and concert what measures must be taken for your Royal Highness's security."

While awaiting John MacDonald's return, Boradale and his wife did their best to make the Prince comfortable in the wretched habitation which was now their only home, and Charles as usual was very cheerful and appreciative. But in the small hours of the following morning, Boradale awakened him with bad news. His scouts had reported to him that both Old MacKinnon and Captain John MacKinnon had been captured by the soldiers, and that Charles had been traced from Skye to the mainland.

" I dare not permit you to remain here another hour," he added in great agitation, " for it is plain that the hunt after you is very close. There is a secret place on my land which we call MacLeod's Cave, and by your leave we will go there at once, and there you may lie hid until we see whether my son has found Glenaladale."

So, without even waiting for breakfast, he led Charles up a steep hill which was thickly covered with trees, and so brought him to this secret place, which was a sort of cave in the hillside, commanding a great view of the surrounding country, so that any man concealed there could not be approached without warning. It was only four miles from Boradale's bothie, so that his gillies or servants could go backwards and forwards in very little time with food and news.

Next day, Boradale's son, John MacDonald, came to the secret place, followed by a very tall, handsome gentleman in a rich French coat over his trews, and a three-cornered hat, with tarnished silver braid, upon his head. He had a swaggering, devil-may-care sort of manner, and a look which dared any man to meddle with him. This was Major MacDonald of Glenaladale himself, and Charles was overjoyed to see him again, for he was the very man to have as a companion in any sort of danger, being always cheerful, bold, and daring. Besides, he was a very polished gentleman, speaking French and English fluently, and though Charles had grown to love the Gaelic, he had never learnt to speak it very well, and it was good to be able to converse again with someone who spoke his own language without difficulty.

"Sir," said Glenaladale, lifting his hat and quickly replacing it, "no formalities and no titles in present circumstances, if you please. Time enough for these when we have set your father on his throne again, and come to pay our respects at St James's Palace."

"That day is further off than when last we met, Glenaladale," replied Charles sadly.

" Hoots ! " said the other. " We've beaten the red-
coats many a time in pitched battle, and we'll contrive to
beat them at their hunting of yourself. But it's a wearisome hunt for the quarry, Sir, for you must stay in no
place for long. Your presence in this neighbourhood is
suspected; I learned that on my way hither. Clanranald's country is the place for you, for it is so mountainous that so far the red-coats have left it alone.
Young Clanranald is in hiding there himself just now, and
I know where he is to be found. We'll send a message
to him to meet us, and then we will follow upon the
messenger's heels."

Ranald, Boradale's other son, gladly undertook to
deliver this message, and after giving him some hours'
start, Charles, accompanied by Glenaladale and Boradale,
set out on his travels once more. That night they lay in
the heather not far from Clanranald's country, and as they
had no food, Boradale offered to go and buy some at a
clachan in the neighbourhood. He did not return until
the following morning, and when he came he brought,
not food, but the very worst of tidings.

" No less than six ships-of-war are anchored in Loch
Nevis," said he with a distracted air, " they having
followed your Royal Highness from the Isles. But
there is worse in it than that. So certain are the soldiers
that you are in this district, that there is a cordon of
troops flung completely round it, with sentinels stationed
every half mile from the head of Loch Eil to the head of
Loch Hourn. Patrols march up and down between the

sentinels to keep them to their duty, and every ford and pass is guarded."

" Then there is no getting to Clanranald's country," observed Glenaladale, looking unusually grave, " for we are now cut off from it by the troops."

" It seems to me that there is no getting anywhere," said Charles, " since it is plain that we are in a trap."

Glenaladale smiled at him and clapped him on the shoulder.

" Hoots ! " said he. " The hunter sets many a trap from which the quarry contrives to escape. With the help of God and our own wits, we'll cheat this red-coated hunter of his spoil."

He stood up and snuffed the air like a stag at bay.

" I know these mountains," said he, " better than do the red soldiers, and in my youth I learned to climb them like the deer. They are full of perils to the stranger, but to their own people they are the best friends in the world, with their mists, and their hidden corries, and their inaccessible fastnesses. Trust in them, Sir, and in me, and myself and the mountains will get you out of this trap."

" I am well content to do so," replied Charles cheer-fully, " for the Highland hills have been kind to me in the past, and I could not have a better guide than Major MacDonald of Glenaladale."

But all the same he did not see how he was ever to break through the cordon of troops which hemmed him in.

10

The Cordon of Troops

Just before they were ready to set out, Boradale's son John, who had been scouting in the neighbourhood, brought to them Lieutenant John MacDonald, Glenaladale's younger brother, whom he had happened to meet, and who was very anxious to assist in aiding the Prince. It was agreed, therefore, that three attendants being the most Charles could have with him for safety on this stage of his wanderings, Boradale himself should return home. His house having been burnt so recently, it was clear that he was a marked man, and if he was long away from his native place, enquiries might be made. So he and his son Ranald said good-bye to Charles, who set out with Glenaladale, his brother, and Boradale's son John; they struck northwards, for Glenaladale was of the opinion that their best chance was to try to cut through the cordon and get to Poolewe, or to some other port on the north-west coast, where it was possible that the Prince would find a ship for France.

Their way lay through some of the most mountainous parts of the Highlands, and reminded Charles of the time when Ned Burke had led him, with the two captains, into the hills of Coradale on the Long Isle. At all costs they must avoid the passes and glens, and so they must be for ever climbing and scrambling, leaping from stone to stone over the burns, wading through waist-high bracken, and going on hands and knees over rock which had an awful precipice beneath. Glenaladale set the pace, and it was a hot one, so hot that even Charles, active and young and used by now to every hardship, could hardly keep up with him. When they came to places where they could be seen from the glens below, they must bend double as they walked, so that their backs ached and pains of cramp shot through them from the unnatural position. At other times, Glenaladale would drop on his stomach and worm his way through the heather like a snake, signalling to the rest to follow suit.

As the sun rose higher in the heavens, and the cool of the dawn turned into the heat of a July day, the journey became all but intolerable. Sweat caked the Prince's hair, his clothes stuck to him, and his eyes were blinded by perspiration. Whenever they came to a burn, they paused for a moment to suck up the water in their mouths and to splash their chests and wrists with it, but in a few moments they would be as thirsty and hot as ever, for there were no trees on these heights, and the sun beat down upon them without mercy. Charles was almost spent when, about mid-day, Glenaladale threw himself down among the rocks and mountain herbs at the top of a great hill, and in a voice harsh with dust and fatigue, told them they might rest.

They lay there for some time, the breath whistling in their throats, and the sweat from their bodies wetting the heather on which they sprawled. Like dead men they lay there, not moving or speaking, until at last Glenaladale sat up and said :

" When it comes night, we shall be needing food, for a man cannot travel in this way without sustenance. John," he went on, addressing his brother, " go you down into Glenfinnan, get some oatmeal and butter, and if possible some brandy, find out the news, and meet us when night falls at Sgor nan Coireachan in Lochiel's country."

His brother went off at once, and the others, after a little more rest, resumed their exhausting journey. It was some two hours later when, as they clambered along the lower slopes of a hill, they saw below them in a narrow pass a great herd of shaggy black cattle moving along very fast.

" Wait you," muttered Glenaladale to his companions. " Those will be some of my tenants' cattle-beasts, and from the number of them, as also from their being down in the glens at this season of the year, I suspect there is somewhat amiss. Mr MacDonald, do you stay here with his Royal Highness, while I go down-by and see what's afoot."

He went rapidly down the hill, and presently could be seen in talk with one of the men who were driving the cattle. It was plain even from this distance that these people were in some deadly sort of panic. There were women and children among them; they urged the beasts forward with loud cries and flourishing of cudgels, and the man whom Glenaladale had accosted was waving his arms about, pointing backwards along the pass and shaking his fist in that direction. When at last Glenaladale returned to his companions, he was frowning.

"This is a bad business," said he. "These my tenants are come from the country around Loch Arkaig, which is the country for which we have been making, and they are telling me that it is full of soldiers who are narrowly searching it. Therefore are they driving their cattle into the hidden corries, because otherwise the red soldiers would seize them."

"Then we cannot——" began Charles, but he got no farther, for Glenaladale seized his arm, squeezing it so tight that the Prince almost cried aloud with the pain.

"Hush you now," murmured Glenaladale. "Look yonder."

Following the direction of his glance, Charles saw one of the women who had been driving the cattle, clambering up the hillside in their direction. She had a wooden cog or small pail in her hand, and was carrying it carefully as though it contained something she feared to spill.

"Wind your handkerchief about your face to conceal it," whispered Glenaladale rapidly to Charles. "And when she comes up with us, be sure to say nothing. I am not doubting the good faith of any of my tenants, yet I will not trust any women to keep a secret."

In a few minutes the woman joined them. She was a sturdy young Highland girl, with strong, bare arms and legs and a face blackened by the sun and peat-smoke. Glenaladale greeted her very politely, and for a while they talked together in the Gaelic about the evil times and their mutual acquaintances. Then she offered the pail she had brought, which was full of warm milk from one of the cows in the herd. Having drunk some of it, Glenaladale handed the cog first to John MacDonald, and then to Charles, who drank eagerly, being careful to keep his face turned from the girl. Then, with many compliments on both sides, she left them and returned to her people.

When she was out of earshot, Glenaladale said to his companions :

" I have sent one of the herdsmen yonder after my brother to recall him, and another to find out one, Donald Cameron of Glenpean, who is a tacksman of Lochiel's. For he being a man of some substance, he will be able to supply us with the food in which we stand so much in need."

" Donald Cameron of Glenpean ! " repeated Charles. " Why, I stayed a night at his house when I was first upon my wanderings, and was very kindly entertained. But alas, I wish I could meet with his Chief again. Lochiel's death has been a very great sorrow to me."

" Lochiel is not dead whatever," said Glenaladale,

L   161

surprised. "I know not where he is at present, but certainly he escaped from the battlefield of Culloden, and the last I heard of him, he was hiding with the MacDonalds of Glencoe."

This was such a great and joyful surprise to Charles that he forgot for the moment all his own anxieties and troubles. What with this, and the refreshing effects of the milk, he soon fell into a peaceful sleep in the heather, but Glenaladale and John MacDonald stayed awake lest anyone came on them unawares. It was as well that they did, for Charles had not been sleeping very long before one of them shook him violently by the shoulder, and, without a word, pointed down into the pass.

And there, riding through the narrow defile in which the fugitives had seen the cattle so recently, came a troop of soldiers on horseback. Their scarlet coats, falling to their knees and buttoned tightly at the throat to show no shirt, made a bright splash of colour against the dun hill. The swords and pistols slung on their cross-belts twinkled in the sunlight, and, clear in the silence of the afternoon, could be heard the jingle of their stirrup-irons and bits, and the click of a horse's hoof against a stone. An officer rode at their head, in a plumed hat with a black cockade in it; often he stood up in his stirrups and narrowly scanned the surrounding country. At any moment the three fugitives crouched on the hill expected him to spy them, but fortunately the heather concealed them and the troop passed by without suspecting their presence.

As soon as the hoof-beats had died into silence, Glenaladale, without a word, began wriggling his way on hands and knees at a furious pace up the hill, taking advantage of every bit of cover, keeping his head almost level with the ground, and going so skilfully that he seemed to show no more signs of his progress than would a rabbit scuttling to its burrow. The others followed in the same fashion, and so they went on until they were so high upon the hill that they could not be seen from the glens.

" Where now ? " panted Charles, when at last they could pause for a while.

" We'll need to keep to the tops of the mountains," replied Glenaladale, " for here we are free of those red-coated rogues. It is true that even here we may be surprised by the Militia, but they are less to be feared than the soldiers in the sense that many of them, for all they wear the red cross in their bonnets, are no ill friends to your Royal Highness."

" But what of your brother ? " asked John Mac-Donald. " And also of Glenpean, who will be coming to find us ? "

" If they can find us, that is well," replied Glenaladale briskly, " but if not, we must do the best we can without them."

They were now so high upon the mountain-side that they were able to walk upright, which was a great relief, and so was the coolness which had come with evening. But they were all so faint from want of food that their progress was very slow, which indeed it must have been in any case, for with the fading of the light they were in danger of falling on these high peaks with their naked rock. With the coming of night, they began to be as cold as they had been hot before, being several thousand feet above sea-level, and every now and then their feet scrunched in pockets of snow which, at this altitude, never melted even in summer. At about eleven o'clock, the moon broke through scattered clouds and showed them, about a hundred feet below, the figure of a man climbing the mountain in their direction.

" Wait you here," said Glenaladale promptly to his companions; and with the skill of the expert climber, he went rapidly down the rock face to meet the stranger.

When he returned, the stranger was with him, and turned out to be none other than Donald Cameron of Glenpean himself. He was overjoyed at this unexpected reunion with the Prince whom he had sheltered in his house in April; he had been searching for them everywhere, and it was only by chance that he had happened upon them. They asked eagerly for food, but sadly he shook his head, and said that the red soldiers had plundered his house so thoroughly that all he had left to bring was a little oatmeal and about a pound of butter. This was poor fare for starving men, but the Prince had learnt from experience that it was very sustaining, and when he had eaten some of it, his faintness left him. Then Glenaladale explained to Glenpean that they were trying to break through the cordon of troops which surrounded this country; Glenpean, who was deaf, listened with his head on one side, scratched his nose, looked very grave, and said it was impossible.

"That is an ill word to use," Glenaladale rebuked him sharply. "It must be done, and when a thing must be done it cannot be impossible. No man knows this district better than yourself, and I am sure that if you think well upon it, you will hit upon some means of getting us out."

"Indeed and there is one way I know of," replied Glenpean, scratching his nose harder than ever and looking very worried, "but while the three of us might make it without mishap, I am at thinking that his Royal Highness will hardly manage it. For we must be at climbing over one of the most dangerous mountains in the whole of the Highlands."

"Where the rest of you can go, so can I," said Charles, smiling at him; "especially with so good a guide. So do you lead the way, Donald, and have no fear for me."

"Well, then," said Glenpean, "I will guide your Royal Highness to that place, for it is the only one for us if we are to break out of this trap."

The four of them continued walking all night, for it was bright moonlight so that they could see their way without much difficulty. Morning found them on a hill called Mammyn Callum, which to his knowledge, said Glenpean, had been searched by the red soldiers only a few days previously, so that it was unlikely that the fugitives would be disturbed if they took some rest here.

But the Prince, though by now he thought he could sleep anywhere, found sleep impossible to him except in brief snatches all that day, for not only was it boiling hot again, but he could hear the sounds which told him that there were soldiers in the glen below. It was very frightening to lie there and listen to the changing of sentries, the marching up and down of patrols, the words of command, and the confused noise of hammering, clink of steel, and snorting of horses. The day was so still again, that all these sounds seemed to come from near at hand.

At nine o'clock at night they started off again, having eaten nothing but a moorcock which Glenaladale had contrived to catch in a snare and which had to be eaten raw because they dared not light a fire. They walked until one o'clock in the morning, when Glenpean, who now had taken charge of the expedition, said that they must rest again, because they were soon to climb the terrible mountain of which he had spoken, and for this they would need all their strength.

" The worst that is in it is this," he went on frankly. " That we must be at making the climb before the light comes, because we have to pass close by the camps of the red soldiers, and yet because of the darkness we shall be lucky if we do not slip and plunge over the precipice."

" I will brave the precipice rather than the red soldiers," said the Prince.

Glenpean made no reply, but he began to scratch his nose again, a habit of his which had amused Charles

166

several times already. Observing that the Prince was watching this performance, Glenpean said solemnly :

" Oh, Sir, my nose is yuicking, which is always a sign with me that we have great hazards and dangers to pass through."

The Prince could not help laughing outright at this.

" Why," said he, " I think your nose is in the right of it at present, Donald. And that is a very good nose you have which gives you warning of peril."

The words had scarcely left his lips before John MacDonald, who had been making a reconnoitre, came running to them in great agitation, and told them that a party of soldiers was climbing the very hill on which they lay concealed.

" There is nothing for it, then, but to break through the cordon without delay," said Glenaladale. " Glenpean, do you go first, since you are now our guide, his Royal Highness next, and Mr MacDonald and I will bring up the rear. You understand we are to pass between two camps in the glen down-by; they are separated from one another by the foot of this perilous mountain we are to climb. So let no man speak one word while we are in their neighbourhood, and let us all take care to move as quietly as possible."

Even as they set off at a rapid pace down the hillside, they saw from behind them the gleam of a torch which was carried by the party of soldiers of whose presence John MacDonald had given them warning. The moon was behind clouds, and this was fortunate, yet the light was sufficient to show Charles the terrible dangers through which he was now to pass. Not far behind him were the soldiers with the torch; in the glen below winked and twinkled the camp-fires of the other troops; and directly facing him there stood up in the dim light the great towering wall of rock which was his only means of cutting through the cordon, its summit veiled in cloud. Its craggy feet thrust forward into the glen, almost bare of trees and heather; it was seamed with gullies, out of which the mist boiled slowly; its smocked face was encrusted with snow, and here and there, as though the mountain wept, rivulets cascaded down it in white ribbons. The foot of it almost cut the glen in two, and it was because of this that at this point in the cordon the camps of the red soldiers were a little farther apart from one another than at other places.

The four men went in single file, bent double again, holding their breath as they approached the bottom of the glen and were within earshot of the soldiers. The agony of that half-hour was the worst Charles had experienced in the whole of his adventures. He was literally in a trap; if a stone dislodged by his foot attracted the attention of the soldiers in the camps, or one of the sentries caught sight of him through a perspective-glass when the moon slipped from behind the clouds, he must be caught, for his retreat was cut off by the party behind him. The sweat broke out upon his body, but not from heat; sheer terror moved in him, and it needed all his will-power to control it. Scarcely had he time to realise with relief that he and his friends had passed out of sight of the two camps, and had gained the rocky foot of the mountain, before the second peril was upon him, a climb seemingly impossible save to the deer.

Ahead of him he observed Glenpean scrambling down into a gully which split the base of the mountain into two. Firs and alders clung to its sides for some hundred feet, and between them was a burn, rushing and twisting its tortuous way through the rock. The going here was difficult and exhausting, but it was not unduly perilous, for the trees provided hand-holds and their roots formed a sort of natural ladder. But presently the trees ended, and Charles saw Glenpean strike out from the gully on to the naked rock-face beside it. And now their pace slowed to a crawl, for it was no longer a case of tedious scrambling. From this point to the summit of the mountain, the way was bare rock, brittle after the wet spring, with the mist swirling about them, a yawning gulf below them, and craggy outthrusts, like the teeth of monsters, defying them on every hand. Each step, each hand-hold, must be tested with care; sometimes they must spring from one precarious perch to another; they dared not pause to rest, for the air was so cold upon these dizzy heights that it froze the hands and feet in a minute. It was like climbing a wall; often one foot would swing in space while the eye tried frantically to see through the mist where next to place it. The rush and chatter of the rivulets alone broke the eerie silence, and little clouds, enveloping each figure in an airy prison, and drenching them with moisture, frequently hid each from his companions.

They had begun this dreadful climb between one and two in the morning. Day broke upon them, and they were but halfway up. But the blessed light of the sun encouraged them, and gave new strength to their exhausted bodies. Mist still boiled out of the gullies and shrouded the summit in a white blanket, but there were patches of clearness in which they could see the gnarled rock-face, wrinkled like an aged woman, the glistening snow which scrunched beneath their feet, and the tooth-like ridges round which they must wind their way.

After another hour, they came to a place where they must cross a mountain stream wider than any they had encountered hitherto. It gushed forth in a vicious white cascade, filling the air with spray, and making a sound like thunder. The party halted, as, with infinite skill and caution, Glenpean began to cross it first, sometimes springing from one stone to another, at others going on all fours and worming his way half in and half out of the water. He landed safely at last on the other side, and turning, beckoned Charles to follow him. The Prince was by this time so weary that his head felt light and his vision swam. There seemed to be no strength left in his limbs, and every movement was an effort. Somehow he reached the middle of the stream, and, crouching on a slippery rock, with the spray blinding him and the water pouring by on every side with terrifying force, prepared to make the long leap which must take him to the next. He had gathered himself for the spring, when one foot slipped just as he was taking off. He clutched frantically at the air to save himself; the other foot plunged into the water, and the force of it, falling almost perpendicularly down the mountain, swept him with it.

In one horrible moment he saw below him the boundless space, the savage rocks, the glen dwindled to a mere thread, and a pinpoint of light which told of the campfires of his foes. Then the view reeled and spun, and his senses left him. But even as he plunged to certain death, one leg encountered a half-submerged rock; his fainting instinct hooked his leg around it, and held fast. His face was in the water and he gasped and choked, his hands fighting and groping to lift himself. Then other hands, strong and skilful, were thrust under his shoulders, and he felt himself being dragged and pulled to safety.

" Yon was a narrow squeak," said a voice beside him, and he saw the white face of Glenaladale twisting itself into a grin.

It was broad day when at last they reached the summit of this terrible mountain, and in a hidden corrie whither Glenpean guided them, they dropped down in their tracks and lay exhausted. All day they lay there, rising only to refresh themselves at a burn; weak from fatigue and lack of food, they had no strength left to talk to one another or to discuss their future plans. To the Prince it was enough that they had broken out of the trap which seemed to have closed its teeth fast upon him. His hands and feet were cut from the climb, his limbs were weak as water, his body was bruised from his fall, and he was sick and shaken; yet, secure upon this mountain-top, three thousand feet above the heads of his enemies, he was able to sleep at last, and in sleep to regain some strength for what was coming.

At night they rose again, and staggering with their weakness as though they were drunk, pushed on slowly across the mountains through the hours of darkness, going always northwards, towards Poolewe and a possible ship for France. When morning dawned again, they found themselves in Glenshiel, and after some hours' rest, Glenpean offered to go and seek for food and news. He returned at evening, bringing with him some bannocks, butter, and a leathern bottle containing usquebaugh, which was the Highland name for whisky. He brought also an acquaintance of his, Donald MacDonald, who told the Prince that there had been a French ship at Poolewe only a few days previously, but no one knowing what was become of his Royal Highness, she had taken off some other fugitives and had sailed away again.

"Perhaps she will return," said Charles, trying to be cheerful under this disappointment. "At any rate, our best plan is still to make for Poolewe and lie concealed in the neighbourhood in case this ship or another one comes into the port."

"That will not do at all," said Donald MacDonald flatly. He was a very tall, thin man, with a face pitted with smallpox scars. "The red soldiers are thick about

He clutched frantically at the air to save himself.

the ports, and the search for your Royal Highness is hotter there than at any other place. And certainly you cannot be staying where you are; for I must tell you that all this day you have been lying within cannon-shot of two small camps of the soldiers."

" Instead of telling us what we cannot do," said Glenaladale irritably, " be telling us what we can do, Donald MacDonald. For I suppose that Glenpean did not bring you to visit us only to put despair upon us all."

Donald MacDonald was rather offended at this, and it was some while before he could be induced to offer any suggestion. Then, turning his back upon Glenaladale, he said to the Prince :

" Has your Royal Highness ever heard of the Seven Men of Glenmoriston ? "

" No," replied Charles, " I have never heard of them, I think. Who may they be ? "

" I will not be at telling you their names," answered Donald, sinking his voice to a whisper, " for they are terrible men whatever if their secret is told. But I will tell your Royal Highness this : Each man of them served in your army; each man had his house burnt over his head by the red soldiers for engaging in your cause. Therefore did they bind themselves together, intent upon revenge, and upon the holy iron they swore to stand together upon every occasion, and to dedicate the remainder of their lives to bringing vengeance upon those who made their hearths desolate, ruined their families, and slew their kin."

"I have heard of them," interposed Glenaladale, "and certainly it is not to be thought of that his Royal Highness should have anything to do with them. They are wild men, robbers and outlaws, and they do not stick at murder. On the bough of many a tree in their neighbourhood may be seen the gory head of a soldier."

"And will you be holding that against them?" asked Donald angrily. "I know them well, for one of them was married upon my sister, and when the red soldiers burnt the clachan where she lived, they drove her out into the snow, with her new-born babe in her arms, so that she died and the bairn with her."

It was plain that a quarrel was brewing between Donald and Glenaladale, so Charles thought it best to intervene.

"I am at this time altogether without plans," said he, "and know not where to go. Do you think these men would assist me, Donald?"

"They would assist your Royal Highness to the last drop of blood in their bodies," replied Donald earnestly, "and they would conceal you in their fastnesses so well that not all German George's soldiers could ever find you. Only, if you put yourself into their hands, you must trust them entirely and abide by their decision in all things. I will not be at concealing from you that they are touchy and proud, owning no man their master, following no chief, and being a law unto themselves. To their enemies they are fierce and bloody, and so great has become the terror of their name, that there is not a man in Scotland will drink with them. But your Royal

Highness will find no better friends, if you will trust them."

" I am," said Charles, smiling, " an outlaw like themselves. Moreover, I cannot help remembering that when I came to Scotland to try to win back my father's throne, I brought with me just seven men. I was told that I was mad, yet I came near to conquering a kingdom. And now that I am altogether destitute, I find another seven men willing to aid me. That's a good omen, I believe. How say you, Glenpean? Is your nose yuicking to warn you of danger if I place myself in the hands of the Seven Men of Glenmoriston ? "

" It is not yuicking at all just now," replied Glenpean gravely.

" Then, Donald," said the Prince, " you shall lead me to these outlaws, and I will be content to trust them to the uttermost and put myself unreservedly into their hands."

11

The Seven Outlaws

VERY early the next morning they set out, being somewhat refreshed by the food and whisky. Donald
Cameron of Glenpean took his leave of them, not being
able to guide them any further upon their way, and they
put themselves in the charge of Donald MacDonald.

They had not gone very far when Glenaladale, with a
sharp exclamation, clapped his hand to his pocket and
cried out that he had lost his purse.

"By heaven!" he exclaimed, "this is a great misfortune. It contained all the money we had between
the four of us, and we are quite lost without it. There
is but one thing to do now, and that is to return to the
place where we passed the night and make a search for it."

"Nay, you might search for hours," objected the
Prince, "and yet not find it among all that heather and
bog."

But Glenaladale refused to continue the journey without going back to look for his purse, so as there was
no sense in the four of them going, Charles sat down
some distance from the track with Donald MacDonald,

while Glenaladale and John MacDonald set off on their seemingly hopeless search. They had not been gone many minutes before the sound of voices and the clink of steel approaching their resting-place in the heather, made the Prince and his companion throw themselves flat on their faces and crouch there as quiet as mice. Peeping through the bushy stalks of the bog-myrtle in front of them, they saw coming along the track an officer of the red soldiers followed by two privates. Their white gaiters were sadly stained from their walk, and the queues or pigtails of their wigs were untidy. They were talking together in Lowland Scots, which sounded strange to Charles after the Gaelic and the halting English to which he had been accustomed for so long.

" Nae dout o' it at a'," the officer was saying, as he came level with the Prince's hiding-place, " I ken fine Charlie Stuart's i' these pairts, and some lucky body's gaeing tae earn himsel' a bonny price for catching him, thirty thousand pounds—ay, my lads, nae less than thirty thousand English pounds. Losh, and I wish it might be mysel'."

He strode on, blissfully unconscious that the man with this price on his head was within ten yards of him at that very moment.

" Glenaladale and John MacDonald will meet them face to face," whispered Charles in great anxiety to his companion, as the sound of the three soldiers' voices died away.

" It would have been the whole party of us would

have done that," replied Donald, "but for the lost purse, and so I am at thinking that it was the Great Being Himself Who caused him to lose it."

As they waited there, one of those sudden hill mists, so common in the Highlands, came drifting over to them, and in a few moments the whole scene around them was blotted out, and they could not see a yard before their faces. Soaked and blinded, they remained in their concealment, and when presently they again heard footsteps approaching them they dared not call out to enquire if it was their friends, in case it was the soldiers returning. The footsteps came on, making directly towards them, and as Charles made to rise, being determined, if it were the enemy, to put up some defence, a man's figure loomed up out of the fog and cannoned into him, nearly knocking him over. With a gasp of relief he heard a familiar voice exclaim angrily, and then the rasp of a sword being drawn from its scabbard.

"Glenaladale!" cried the Prince. "It is myself and Donald MacDonald. Thank God you are safe, man, for soldiers have passed close by us, and we feared you must encounter them."

"We saw nothing of those rogues," replied Glenaladale, replacing his sword. "But we found my purse, so it seems that Providence must still be watching over us."

They pursued their way across the mountain, often having to go slowly because of the mist, but Donald MacDonald knew every yard of this country and never led them astray. When they were come within some few miles of Glenmoriston, he said that he would go and seek the Seven Men, and ask them if they would be willing to give hospitality to three unfortunate gentlemen who were fugitives from Culloden. He was gone an hour, and when he returned, he reported that he had found three of the Seven Men in a cave of theirs at Coiredhogha, the other four being out a-foraging, and that they had invited the fugitives to join them there.

" They have not a word of the English," said Donald, " so that one of us three will need to be interpreter when your Royal Highness desires to converse with them. You may not be at liking the looks of them at first, but I do promise you they will prove stout and faithful, and will give you better hospitality than you can find in many a gentleman's house."

It was evening again when, scrambling in single file up the scree of a mountain slope, the four fugitives saw their way barred by three outlandish figures. They were men, but they looked more like bears, so shaggy were they with beards and whiskers and their long hair falling upon their shoulders in wild tangles. Their dress was composed of the skins of animals, slung about them in a careless fashion and their bare legs and arms were burnt black from exposure. Stuck in their belts of raw leather were dirks and pistols, and each man leaned upon a musket. Their expression was formidable and savage, and they looked so much like wild men of the woods that the Prince felt he would rather have encountered even the red soldiers than these fierce barbarians.

And then, to complete his dismay, the three of them, ignoring his companions, and uttering frenzied exclamations in the Gaelic, came bounding down the hillside towards him, and, pushing the others aside, in an instant surrounded him. For a moment he wondered if they were going to tear him in pieces, thinking him some spy, but he quickly saw it was quite otherwise. One seized his hand in a grip like a vice, the second embraced him in a hug like a bear's, while the third, dancing around him like a lunatic, uttered cries which, though Charles could not understand them, plainly were those of welcome.

"They know you," said Donald MacDonald, "and are telling you that this is the happiest moment of their lives, because they believed you dead."

Charles smiled at the wild men, gave each in turn his hand to shake, and, in halting Gaelic, told them that he had come to them to beg for their assistance. Still chattering excitedly, the three men made him understand by signs that they would escort him at once to their hiding-place, and so, one of them leading the way, and often turning back to beckon with an encouraging grin, the little procession proceeded up the mountain-side, until suddenly the first man, stooping down, disappeared from view. When Charles came to the spot, he found that the tall bracken hid an opening in the rock, and finding that he was expected to enter this, he crawled through it and in a moment found himself standing in a surprisingly large cave. It was quite light, because the opening on the other side was much larger than the one by which he had entered, and through the middle of it, deep in a rocky bed, ran a fine purling stream. In spite of this, the cave was dry, and formed a perfect natural habitation. Its contents were characteristic of its wild tenants; muskets and bayonets were slung upon the wall, powder-horns and bags of bullets were piled in a corner; and in another corner lay a collection of articles obviously once belonging to the red soldiers, for there was a knapsack, a water-flask, and a pair of military boots.

Above a fire which had been kindled in the cave, hung a large earthern pot from which there escaped a lovely odour of cooking. The fugitives were so hungry, having eaten nothing but a little oatmeal and butter for so long, that this smell made them forget everything else in their desire for a good meal. Charles made them all sit down in a circle with himself, and he would not let the three men wait on him, nor would he permit them to observe the formality due to his rank. They all ate heartily of mutton, cheese, and venison, warming themselves with the whisky of which the outlaws seemed to have a plentiful supply. When the meal was finished, one of the outlaws took Glenaladale aside, and spoke earnestly to him; presently he said:

"These men have been telling me that they will be taking an oath of fidelity and secrecy to your Royal

Highness, and I beg you will indulge them, for they insist upon it, and such things mean much to them."

So, drawing his dirk, he handed it first to John Mac-Donnell, who seemed to be the leader of the outlaws, and who, taking the weapon in his outstretched palm, solemnly kissed it, and repeated in Gaelic the oath which Glenaladale administered to him, for Charles's benefit, in English :

" That your back shall be to God and your face to the Devil; that all the curses the Scriptures did pronounce may come upon you and all your descendants, if you will not stand firm to the Prince in the greatest dangers, and if you should disclose to any person, man, woman, or child, that the Prince was in your keeping, till once his person shall be out of the country."

Then the other two men, Alexander MacDonnell and Alexander Chisholm, likewise took this terrible oath, each fervently kissing the ' holy iron ' before doing so.

" Why," said Charles, when the ceremony was over, " since we are all in equal danger, methinks that I and my friends here should take an oath in our turn, swearing that if danger comes upon us we will all stand by our kind hosts to the last drop of our blood."

Glenaladale interpreted this to the three outlaws, but they shook their heads most violently. All they asked from Charles was, first that he would put himself un-reservedly into their hands and be guided by them in all matters appertaining to his safety, and secondly that whatever he said in English might be translated for them by Glenaladale or one of the others. They on their part wished that all they said might be interpreted to the Prince, and that thus there should be no secrets of any kind between them.

Charles slept soundly that night, lulled by the murmur of the stream which flowed beside his bed of bracken, and comforted by the security of his hiding-place. Next morning, the other four outlaws returned from their foraging; two of them, who were brothers to Alexander Chisholm, and whose names were Hugh and Donald, were dragging between them the carcase of an ox, the third, Patrick Grant, commonly called Black Peter of Craskie, a great giant of a man, came bowed beneath the weight of a full-grown stag, and the fourth, Gregor M'Gregor, was burdened with a case of whisky. Being presented to the Prince, they greeted him in the same enraptured manner as had their companions, and immediately took the same oath to him on their dirks.

" Why," said Charles merrily, " I have now the first Privy Council I have had since my defeat at Culloden, and I promise you, as is the duty of kings and princes, never to act without consulting my Council and seeking their advice."

The Prince had come to the Seven Men of Glenmoriston upon July 24th, and he lived with them, sometimes in one of their caves, sometimes in another of their hiding-places, until the first week in August. Donald MacDonald had returned home, but Glenaladale and

John MacDonald remained with him, and took it in turns to act as sentries while the Seven Men went out a-scouting or to fetch in food. The amount of food they brought, and which consisted, besides venison and game-birds, of mutton, fine bread, beef, and many small luxuries, puzzled Charles, until they told him that they stole these things from the camps of the red soldiers, even sometimes venturing to make a raid upon the great garrison at Fort Augustus. They were very proud of this thieving, partly because it displayed their boldness and courage, and partly because it satisfied their desire for revenge. The Prince could not altogether blame them for their robberies, but he was very upset when they boasted of murder as well.

Perceiving his distress, they endeavoured to justify themselves by telling him dreadful stories of the brutalities of the soldiers after the Battle of Culloden. At the command of their officers, the soldiers had butchered in cold blood all the wounded lying on the battlefield, leaving their bodies unburied; a party of fugitives taking refuge in a barn, they had put guards around it and set fire to it, burning alive all who were in it; the bodies of the slain were plundered of money, jewels, and even clothes; and the prisoners herded into Inverness were denied food or drink or a surgeon to tend their wounds. Other stories told to the Prince by the Seven Men were too horrible to repeat, especially those which concerned the treatment of women and children. Yet though Charles knew that they were true, and understood how

185

the outlaws felt about this treatment of their people, he tried very hard to persuade them that vengeance should be left to God, and that one murder does not excuse another.

So great a love and admiration had these wild, ferocious outlaws conceived for the Prince, that they listened to him meekly, and took in very good part his rebukes for their un-Christian conduct. They did not understand his point of view, but because it distressed him, they refrained from boasting of their deeds of blood. Not only was he their lawful Prince, but during the time he was with them he showed himself their superior in the manly arts of wrestling and sword-play, outdid them in his skill at hunting and in shooting birds upon the wing, and taught them many things about the art of cookery and simple surgery. Added to this was his coolness in danger, his endurance of hardship, and his persistent cheerfulness, so that altogether they regarded him with something approaching worship.

One day the Seven Men returned to the hiding-place where they had left the Prince, driving no less than sixty head of cattle before them, and loaded with bread and cheese and whisky. They were eager to tell the Prince the tale of how they had come by these spoils, and as they assured him that there was no bloodshed in it, he listened with great interest and astonishment while Glenaladale interpreted the story which Patrick Grant related in Gaelic.

"This morning early," said Patrick, "we met with a

herd-boy upon the hill of Lundy, who told us that a great party of the red soldiers, with some of the Militia, had taken away all my uncle's cattle, and were driving them to Fort Augustus. Scarcely had he told us this, than down in the narrow pass below us, we saw these red-coated thieves herding their spoil. We made down to them with all speed until we were come within musket-shot of them, when we roared out to them with a volley of oaths which made all the rocks resound, bidding them leave the cattle and march off. The officers immediately drew up their men to engage us, and sent one of them to let us know that if we would surrender we should have protection. Upon this I cocked my piece at the messenger and swore by Him that made me that I should give them all protections which would serve them to the Day of Judgment, adding that we would have no other terms but that the whole party should immediately retire and leave the cattle to us, and that if they did not, it would be the worse for them, because we had a great party of men in our rear who were coming up to our assistance. This," said Patrick, shooting an apologetic glance at the Prince, " was a lie, for we had no such thing whatever."

" I think it is what is called a white lie, Patrick," observed Charles, smiling.

" When the messenger returned to his officer," continued Patrick, encouraged, " the march was instantly beat upon their drums, and the soldiers continued on their way, still driving the cattle before them. So we, being much enraged, fired upon them from behind our rocks, which obliged the officers to call another halt and to draw up their men a second time. But by this time some of the soldiers had the fear upon them, and began to throw down their arms and run away, and seeing this, the officers sent a second messenger to us, demanding of us were we mad to make such an assault upon the King's forces, being so few in number as we were. To this we answered: 'If German George, whom you call your King, were here, he should meet the same treatment at our hands as we are giving you.' And we told him that they must give us the cattle, or we would continue firing upon them all the way to Fort Augustus. Understanding that we were in earnest, and seeing the impossibility of returning our fire because we were above them and well sheltered by our rocks, the officers bade their men leave the cattle in our hands, but we were not satisfied with this, being resolved to teach them a lesson for their defiance of us, and so we demanded likewise a case of whisky and some sacks of bread and cheese, telling them we were as ready to shoot them for the provisions as we had been for the cattle. The officers then thought fit to bid their men leave the provisions on the ground for us to collect when they were gone, and so we bade them farewell, keeping them covered till they were out of sight, and desired of them that if they passed that way again, they would be sure to bring provisions with them, since these were very welcome to us."

The Prince could not but admire the boldness of such men, who, though there were but seven of them, could successfully defy a hundred soldiers. But happy though he was with the outlaws, and secure though he felt in their protection, he knew that his duty was still to escape from Scotland, and that it was a duty which became more urgent every day. The summer was nearly ended; the birds were restless and were beginning to migrate; soon the autumn rains would come, and then the snow, and when the cold and the darkness of winter returned, he would not be able to skulk in the mountains. But when he sent one of his companions to enquire if there were any more French ships come in, he heard that there were not any at Poolewe or at the other ports on the north-west coast. At last it was Glenaladale who suggested another plan which, though it might not get the Prince out of Scotland, might place him under a more powerful protection than that of these poor outlaws.

" I have heard," said he to the Prince, " when I was out to-day seeking for news, that Lochiel is now in the company of MacPherson of Cluny, and that the two of them are in Cluny's country of Badenoch. Now it sticks in my mind that we should try to make our way to them, for though they are both ruined for their loyalty to your Royal Highness, their clans are large and remain faithful to them, and therefore your Royal Highness would be safer in their midst than anywhere else in Scotland."

Charles agreed readily to this suggestion, chiefly because he was so very anxious to meet with Lochiel again, who was his favourite among all the chiefs who had fought for him. But when Glenaladale informed the seven outlaws of what was proposed, they shook their heads and frowned. They did not know, they said, the way to Cluny's country; they might fall into the hands of the red soldiers if they set out without knowing the route; and for all anyone knew to the contrary, Lochiel and Cluny might have moved on again. It was plain that they were jealous of the Prince's placing himself in any other hands than their own, and that in their simple minds they had become convinced that he would be content to live with them for ever, and share the simple, lawless life with which he had seemed so content the last few weeks.

When Glenaladale tried to argue with them, they turned sulky and almost fierce; they swore that they would rather keep the Prince a prisoner than let him proceed until they deemed it safe; and then, turning to Charles, they reminded him of the promise he had made them not to act without their advice. Glenaladale turned angry in his turn, and it nearly came to a drawing of dirks, but the Prince's tact saved the situation. He told the Seven Men that if they insisted upon it he would stay with them until they gave the word for him to move on, but if he did, at some time or another he would be bound to be captured, and then there would never be another chance for him to try and regain his father's throne and free Scotland from the yoke of German George.

As very often happens in life, his kindness and under-standing of their point of view was much more effective than if he had reproached them with selfishness, and after consulting for some time amongst themselves, they came to him and said that they were willing to escort him to Badenoch, and would continue to act as his guard until they had placed him safely in the hands of Lochiel or Cluny. They were not at all sure of the way, except for that part of it which lay through their own Glenmoriston, but they would do their best, and would send one of their number on beforehand to try to find out more certain information concerning Lochiel's whereabouts.

So the whole party, which consisted of the Prince, the Seven Men, Glenaladale, and John MacDonald, set off southwards on a wandering which lasted for nearly three weeks. Sometimes they were entertained by the young folk at the shieling-huts, high up in the mountains, and shared their simple diet of cheese, fresh milk and cream, with a little oatmeal. Sometimes they made their camp in the heather and lived upon whatever game they could shoot; and often they most narrowly escaped the patrols of the red soldiers. It was a wearisome wandering, for the weather was pouring wet again, and the first cold of autumn was in the wind. In their ignor-ance of the way, there were days when they wandered in circles; but at long last, upon August 27th, Patrick Grant, who had gone on before them to seek out Lochiel, returned to them and said that Lochiel's brother, Dr Archibald Cameron, awaited them in a wood in the Braes of Achnacarie. When they came there, Dr Cameron told them that Lochiel was in hiding about thirty miles distant, in the care of Cluny and MacPherson of Breackachie, and that Lochiel begged his Royal Highness to come to this hiding-place without delay.

It was cheerful news for the Prince, but he saw that it was quite otherwise to his faithful outlaws, and because he had grown very fond of them, and was extremely grateful to them for all that they had done for him, his own joy was damped. He could not take them with him, because it would be unfair to Cluny to give him this added burden, and besides he knew enough about the Highland people by this time to realise that Cluny and the outlaws, though both had fought for him, might be very ill friends. In those days the Highlands were not a nation at all, but a collection of tribes, nearly all of whom were at feud with one another. Few of them remembered how these feuds had started, for they were centuries old, but they were taught from the cradle to observe them, and it was considered no less of a sacred duty to dirk your enemy than to defend your own kin to the death.

Moreover, besides the possibility that Cluny and the outlaws might harbour ancient grudges, there was the fact that the outlaws had made their name so terrible throughout the Highlands that no man was their friend. They were become what were called broken men, of no clan and owning no chief; their one loyalty was to the Prince for whom they had fought and for whom they had lost everything. Living on whatever they could steal, they had offended everybody, and trusted no one except their own little company. And now when it came to the time for parting, their care for the welfare of their lawful Prince was overridden by a feverish desire to have him remain with them for ever, they who had nothing else to prize; they came to him in a body, and made Charles an appeal which, even though it had to be interpreted to him, was eloquent of their great love.

" Stay with us ! " they cried. " Stay with us for ever ! The mountain of gold which German George has set upon your head might induce the chiefs and gentlemen to betray you, for they can go to a distant country and live on the price of their dishonour. But we can speak no language but our own; we can live in no country save this one; and were we to injure a hair of your head, the very mountains, our friends and refuge, would fall upon us and crush our bones in revenge. Stay with us ! Forget the softness and luxury of France, your royal blood, your father's throne in London, the noise of cities and the compliments of courtiers. With us you shall live like the deer upon the hill, free of all care save how to escape the hunter."

So deep an affection had Charles conceived for these poor outlaws, and so sick was he at heart to think upon exile in France again, that almost he was tempted to comply with their wild appeal. But the call of duty was strong within him; his father waited for him in an agony of anxiety in France; and though he had failed in

N   193

his brave attempt to regain the throne of England, he knew he must never give up trying while he had life.

So, in halting Gaelic, he comforted the Seven Men as best he could, thanked them for all that they had done for him, and cutting the buttons from his waistcoat, gave one to each as a keepsake. These fierce, lawless men wept as he shook their hands in turn, and in voices broken by emotion, they prayed to God to preserve him in all his wanderings and perils.

12

The Cage of Cluny MacPherson

GUIDED by Dr Cameron, and still accompanied by Glenaladale and the faithful John MacDonald, Charles set out that same night towards the hiding-place of Lochiel.

The moon was in its last quarter, and rose about half-past nine; by its faint light they traversed a wild country of mountains and glens, scrambling up hill-paths, or following the drove-roads which were made by the hooves of the cattle when they were driven to the sales in the South; sometimes they saw the gleam of camp-fires which told them of the presence of the red soldiers, and sometimes they saw, shadowy and silent, herds of deer moving on the bare slopes above them. All night they walked, and all next day as well, until, at evening of that day, August 29th, they reached the foot of Ben Alder, which was more like a range of mountains than a single hill, clothed in parts with forest, in others bare and rocky, without habitation save for herdsmen's bothies, and full of corries where, in the days before Charles's coming to Scotland, MacPherson of Cluny had grazed a hundred ponies, many head of cattle, and flocks of sheep and goats. But the bothies were deserted now, and in the corries lived only the deer, the mountain hares, and the great golden eagles.

They camped for the night in the heather, and next morning, still guided by Dr Cameron, they climbed the hill towards a bothie in which, said their guide, Lochiel lay hidden.

Now, Lochiel had been wounded in both legs at Culloden, and though it was more than four months since the battle, he was still so lame that he was really a cripple, and could not walk without support. Therefore, when his henchman, or principal servant, Allan Cameron, told him that he had seen through the doorway of the bothie a party of four men approaching up the hill, but that they were too far off at present for him to see who they were, Lochiel who, like the Prince, was determined never to be captured alive, and who knew that a party of the Militia was encamped only five miles away, struggled up from his bed of heather and prepared to sell his life dearly. There were twelve muskets in the bothie and several pistols; he gave order that these should be loaded, and levelled through the cracks in the turf walls of the bothie, ready to be discharged if, when the approaching party came within range, they were seen to be of the Militia. For because of his lameness he could not escape.

So it was that the Prince and his companions, when they were within a few hundred yards of the bothie, noticed the wicked round barrels of muskets sticking through the apertures. The sight was so unexpected and so daunting, for they were without cover themselves and could be mown down without a chance of resistance, that Charles, halting in his tracks, gave a smothered exclamation of dismay. For one horrible moment he remembered the words of the Seven Men of Glenmoriston, of how they had hinted that perhaps some chief or gentleman might be tempted to betray him for the sake of the huge reward of thirty thousand pounds. He could not doubt Lochiel's loyalty, but it was possible that Lochiel might have had to move from here since Dr Cameron had left him, and that other men, soldiers or the Militia or some traitors, had got into that hut.

But then he heard Dr Cameron give a great shout in the Gaelic. Charles did not understand it, and it was just as well that he did not, because in the English it was " Sons of the hounds, come here and get flesh ! ", which, in the circumstances, would have sounded to him a very sinister invitation. Actually it was the Cameron slogan or war-cry, and on hearing it, the party in the hut knew that the men approaching them were friends.

The echo of this cry was still reverberating in the hills when the doorway of the bothie was darkened by a man's figure. It was wrapped in a plaid, and with a great feeling of joy and relief Charles recognised the dull red and purple of the Cameron tartan. Then the man, supported by another, came limping down the slope towards him; and in another moment he was face to face with Donald Cameron of Lochiel, the Chief of Clan Cameron, and one of the greatest gentlemen in Scotland.

"Oh, my dear master!" cried Lochiel, the tears of joy and physical weakness running down his cheeks. His face was drawn with pain, and his body as thin as a skeleton's from long illness and hardship, but it was the face Charles remembered so well, the kind a man trusts with all he has.

Lochiel was struggling to go down upon his wounded knees before the Prince, but Charles caught him in his arms and prevented it.

"Oh no, my dear Lochiel," said the Prince. He was tactful enough to realise that, like most strong men, Lochiel would hate any reference to his present disabled state, so he added: "You don't know who may be looking at us from the tops of yonder hills, and such gestures might hang us all. Come, conduct me to your refuge which, I promise you, I shall find as happy a home, having your company, as that fine house of yours of Achnacarie."

So the party, with Charles supporting the wounded Lochiel on one side, and his servant, Allan Cameron, propping him up on the other, came to the bothie, where they found MacPherson of Breackachie, Lochiel's brother-in-law, and two gillies belonging to Cluny, who at the moment was absent. In a very little while a meal was spread before the hungry fugitives; there was a mutton-ham, beef sausages, cheese, butter, minced collops of deer-meat, and plenty of whisky. Before the meal began, Lochiel handed Charles a cuoch, or Highland drinking vessel made of oak with silver handles, filled with whisky, and the Prince pledged his hosts in a hearty dram. And when, Lochiel presenting him with a silver spoon, which was one of the few treasures he had saved when his house was burnt by the red soldiers, Charles began to eat the minced collops out of the saucepan (the only cooking vessel they had), he cried:

" Now, gentlemen, I live like a prince," which pleased them all very much, because it was not only polite but kind and understanding.

During the meal, Charles asked Lochiel to tell him all his adventures since they had fought together at Culloden. Lochiel was not very willing to do this, because he was a modest man, and very loyal, and he was aware that his own sufferings were not to be compared with those of the Prince for whom he had fought and lost his all. But he said very briefly that during the battle he had been wounded in both legs and would have been murdered in cold blood by the red soldiers after it was over, had not four of his clansmen carried him off the fatal field into a barn. They had been trying to disguise him before taking him farther, when a party of dragoons had surrounded the barn; if the dragoons had entered it, they would have shot him dead, but by the mercy of God they had been called off by their officer to some other duty just as they were about to come in. Afterwards Lochiel had been sheltered by the Mac-Donalds of Glencoe, and he had wandered and hidden in many other places, but had not dared to return to his own country, because he had heard that his house was burnt and a strict watch kept for him there.

"Then it was my good fortune," he concluded, "to fall in with my cousin, MacPherson of Cluny; and it is now near upon three months that I have been here in his country of Badenoch, either in this bothie or at other places in the neighbourhood, and Cluny has so provided for me that I have plenty of everything, as you see. I thank God that your Royal Highness has come safe through so many perils to take a share in Cluny's hospitality."

"And where is Cluny now?" asked the Prince.

Lochiel smiled as he answered:

"Why, Sir, I am not very sure where he is, but I know that he is very busy about building some secure retreat for me, and for himself, where, says he, we could hide all the winter if necessity arose. He is pleased to be very mysterious concerning this retreat; your Royal Highness has some acquaintance with him, and will know that this good friend of ours is somewhat of a child at heart, for all he is in middle life, loving secrets and surprises, and so I have not plagued him with questions, for I am sure that in his own good time he will show me this refuge, and I would not spoil the enjoyment it will be to him to astonish me with its ingenuity."

Charles stayed two days in the bothie with Lochiel and the others; and on the first day of September, MacPherson of Cluny joined them.

His joy and amazement at finding the Prince there were enormous, for he had had no idea that Charles was any-where in the neighbourhood. He was particularly pleased that the Prince had arrived at this particular time, because he had just finished building this mysterious retreat of which Lochiel had spoken. Cluny was a short, bustling, fussy little man, as vain as a game-cock, and with a haughty exterior which hid a very kind heart. Though he was ruined like the other loyal chiefs, and had lost his castle, his estates, and all his possessions for fighting for Charles, he had the air of a victorious ruler rather than that of a hunted fugitive. It was pathetic and yet gallant to see the way in which he behaved to the gillies who were in attendance upon him; ragged and penniless, he still insisted that they treat him like their Chief, dressed and undressed him, washed his feet, and carried his baggage. He ordered them about like chil-dren, storming at them for any little fault, but never failing, when one of them returned to him from some errand, to touch his bonnet to them or take them by the hand. They for their part treated him in the traditional manner, still reverencing and obeying him as their natural ruler, though he was outlawed and powerless.

His attitude to Charles was somewhat comical. Cluny was too sensible to make use, in the circumstances, of the ceremony due from subject to prince, and when addressing him, called him always 'Mr Thomson', even when there was no possibility of his being over-heard. But on the other hand the tone in which he addressed him was so special and respectful and full of meaning, that anyone overhearing him would have known at once that ' Mr Thomson ' was some important personage. Side by side with this deference, Cluny made it abundantly clear that he expected the Prince to fall in with all his plans for his welfare, and he was as offended by the idea of Charles having plans of his own as had been the Seven Men of Glenmoriston. Lastly, his eagerness to show the Prince this mysterious retreat of his was so childlike, that he gave the appearance of a boy playing at hide-and-seek, rather than of a hunted fugitive rescuing the son of his King.

On September 2nd, the party moved to a shieling-hut which stood high in a corrie upon Ben Alder; it was very bad and smoky, and not large enough to accommodate the company with any comfort, though Cluny made the gillies lie out in the heather. Here, however, they had to stay until the 5th, on which date another of Cluny's gillies came to them with the information that it was safe for them to move on at last to Cluny's newly-made refuge. This news made the little man as pleased as if he had been left a fortune; with childish excitement he proclaimed to the Prince that his Royal Highness was now to be conducted to the most safe and ingenious retreat in the whole of the Highlands.

" I call it my Cage," said he. " And when you come to it, Mr Thomson, you will see why."

After Cluny and his gillies had led them over the mountain for about two miles, they came to the foot of a slope of Ben Alder which was very high, rough, and rocky, and which, Cluny informed the Prince, was named ' the slope of the slab of stone '. The lower part of this slope was covered with a thick wood, the trees clinging to the steep ground like sailors to a mast. A hundred feet below the summit, the trees gave place to a naked precipice, of grey, savage, and deeply scarred rock, impassable save to the most experienced climber. And at the very point where the trees ended and the precipice began, Cluny had built his Cage.

It was, indeed, the most cunningly-contrived hiding place, and obviously had taken a great deal of time and trouble to construct. First, some rows of trees had been felled and laid on the ground side by side. The spaces between the trunks had been filled up with earth and stones, packed tight, so that a more or less level floor had been made. Upon this foundation had been built the Cage itself. The walls of it were constructed, partly of a living thicket of holly, which, being an evergreen, would not shed its leaves in winter, and partly of stakes wattled across, and very skilfully joined together with heather ropes and birch twigs. The roof also was wattled, and was thatched thickly with moss. The whole thing was oval in shape, not unlike a great green egg; it clung to the hillside, seemingly fragile and precarious, but actually as firm as the living trees around it, whose roots kept them anchored in the most fantastic attitudes. From whichever angle one looked at it, from above, from below, or from either side, it looked just like an ordinary holly thicket, one of many which grew in those parts; and to complete the ingenuity, two stones standing at a short distance from each other on the side of the precipice had been utilised as a chimney, the smoke from the fire so exactly resembling the colour of the rock and the skeins of mist which always wreathed about these mountains, that no one could distinguish it from below, even on the clearest day.

Such was Cluny's Cage; and it was brave and pitiful to see the way he ushered the Prince into it, for all the world as though it had been that once stately and now ruined castle of his. His coming being perceived by one of his scouts, a gillie was waiting for the party with a beautifully carved wooden bowl, rimmed with silver and filled with milk and cream, the traditional offering of a Highland chief to an honoured guest. Cluny himself, unbonneting and making a bow which would not have disgraced the court of a king, gave 'Mr Thomson' the welcome of his roof-tree and made him free of everything beneath it. When Charles was escorted into the Cage, he found it to be large enough to accommodate five or six persons with comfort; it was furnished with some pieces which Cluny had saved from the destruction of his castle, a table and chairs, and some cooking utensils. For beds there was nothing but piles of heather, but, thanks to the devotion of Cluny's clansmen, there were plenty of provisions, and a burn running beside the Cage provided fresh water.

" Let Butcher Cumberland search the whole of the

Highlands," cried Cluny, as the party sat down to dine, " as skilfully as the hunter searches the mountains for the red deer and the roe, yet never will he be at finding my Cage. Here may you remain in all security, Mr Thomson, for as long as you please, and I shall think myself very honoured to have the entertaining of you; and when the winter comes on, if God in His mercy has not sent a ship by that time, there is another retreat I am after constructing, which is underground, and there we may live defying frost and snow and storm, as snug as the badger in his earth."

Charles was very grateful to Cluny for his kindness and forethought, but he knew he ought not to remain in Scotland a moment longer than was necessary; so it was a relief to him when, that very evening, Cluny himself instructed Glenaladale and John MacDonald to leave the party and go to the coast where, he told them, they were to scout around until they had news of a ship. With the knowledge that these two good friends of his were on the constant watch for a chance of his escape from Scotland, he was very content to stay in the Cage, where he had the congenial company of Lochiel and Cluny, and more comfort than he had enjoyed for a long while. Besides this, he did not feel nearly as much cut off from the outer world as he had done with the Seven Men of Glenmoriston, for Cluny had a constant stream of visitors, all of whom were his own clansmen and therefore to be trusted.

Every morning, one of his gillies who was a barber

came to shave Cluny and his guests, and to give his master the news of the countryside; other gillies acted as scouts, bringing information of the movements of the red soldiers and the Militia; others again brought food, a change of linen, and many little luxuries; and often one or other of the MacPherson clansmen would seek out their Chief to ask advice about their personal affairs, or to beg him to settle some domestic dispute. Cluny listened to them all with great attention, interrupting a meal or a game of cards to give his judgment on a quarrel between two clansmen, or to cuff another soundly for some misdeed. He was as quick to praise as to blame, and whichever he did, the clansman in question took it as meekly and as unquestioningly as a child accepts the verdict of a loving father.

This enduring loyalty and devotion of clansman to chief, made Charles both happy and sad. For since he was a very little boy he had been taught that the only right and natural government in this world was that of one man accepting responsibility for the rest. This, he knew, was the principle of the government called Monarchy. The ruler had the duty of protection; the governed, that of obedience. And the ruler must hold his office by the right of his blood, it being handed down from father to son, so that there should never be any dispute about who ruled next. As a man was master in his own house, so was a king master of his kingdom. He must take decisions, he must accept the heavy burden of deciding on peace or war, the punishment of criminals, and the protection of the weak. He must see the law enforced, and make sure that the rich did not oppress the poor. In return, he had the right to expect a loyalty and submission which no outward circumstances could change; for every man, whether ruler or ruled, has rights as well as duties.

But Charles was sad because he knew that while Cluny, this ruined, penniless, hunted Highland chief, still received from his clansmen the same devotion which they had given him while he was rich and powerful, his own father, the rightful King James the Third of England, had lost the loyalty of many of his subjects only because he was defeated; and he knew also that those subjects could never be happy and secure again until their natural ruler returned to them.

For eight whole days, Charles stayed in the Cage on the slope of Ben Alder. At one o'clock in the morning of the ninth day, September 13th, he was roused from sleep by Cluny, who was beaming all over his face and crying out that there was wonderful news.

13

The Last Adventures

CHARLES was so dazed with sleep, and Cluny, in his excitement, was talking so fast, that for some while the Prince could not understand a word he was saying. Sitting up on his bed of heather, and knuckling at his eyes to get the sleep out of them, he begged Cluny to begin all over again and to speak more slowly.

" I am saying, Mr Thomson," began Cluny, squatting down on his haunches beside the Prince, " that Glenaladale has returned to us, with the news that there is a French ship come into Lochnanuagh on purpose to convey you overseas. She is a privateer, manned entirely by those who have pledged themselves to rescue you, or die in the attempt. Her name is the *Bellona*, and she is commanded by one, Colonel Warren, and she has another ship with her for an escort. Now Colonel Warren has impressed upon Glenaladale that you must make your way to Lochnanuagh with all possible speed, for if word comes to the red soldiers of the presence of these ships, the enemy's men-of-war will be hurrying to the neighbourhood."

"This is good news indeed, Cluny," said the Prince, reaching for his plaid, "and we will start at once, if you please. But how far is it from here to Lochnanuagh?"

"It will not be less than a hundred miles," replied Cluny, "yet by forced marches we can cover the distance in a very little time, for you have shown yourself very good at speedy travelling."

The Prince shook his head at this, and glanced at Lochiel, who lay in another corner of the Cage, wrapped in a profound sleep.

"We can travel only so fast as our good friend there can walk on his lame legs," he said.

At this statement, Cluny's face grew red with exasperation.

"Now, Mr Thomson," said he sharply, "that is the most foolish word I have heard you speak. Have you waited and skulked and starved for so long that now, when a ship is here at last, you will be permitting a friend's lameness to destroy your chance of escape? Consider that the winter is approaching, and that very soon the storms will be preventing any ship from coming to our coasts."

"I have considered it," replied Charles quietly, as he belted the plaid round his waist. "But I have considered also that unless Lochiel is taken overseas, where a proper surgeon may attend to his wounds, he will be lame for life, even if he is not captured. I am resolved, therefore, not to leave Scotland unless I take him with me."

"My grief!" exclaimed Cluny irritably, "Lochiel will be mad at this when he comes to hear of it."

"He will not come to hear of it," retorted Charles sharply, "for I absolutely forbid you, Cluny, to breathe one word to him of what I have been saying."

Cluny's expression on hearing these words was so comical that it was as much as the Prince could do to prevent himself from laughing in his face. For the old Chief was torn between exasperation, injured pride, and the respect due to his Royal Highness; Charles was well aware that Cluny longed to tell him in plain words exactly what he thought of such obstinacy, and because he could not do so, he grew so red in the face and breathed so fiercely in his efforts to control himself, that he looked as though he might explode at any minute.

"We will tell Lochiel and the rest," continued Charles, laying a hand on the Chief's arm and smiling that charming smile of his, "that we needs must travel slowly because I have a return of this dysentery which has, in fact, afflicted me ever since I escaped from Culloden and began my wanderings. Hark you, Cluny; I am leaving Scotland only that I may return to her in happier circumstances, with a brave army at my back, to free her, and England likewise, from the tyranny of this German usurper. If I had my wish, I would stay here for ever, and share your hunted, roving life, for wherever I go, and whatever befalls me, I know that never shall I find such good friends, or a country which I love so dearly, as I have found in the Highlands of Scotland. Yet since duty impels me to go, I am sure you will not add to my burden of sorrow by compelling me to seek my own safety without the comfort of knowing that when I embark on that French ship, such of my friends who are able to do so, may embark with me."

At this appeal of the Prince, Cluny had not one word to say. All he could do was to take the Prince's sunburnt hand and press it hard, sniffing a good deal as though he had a cold. In any case, there was no more time for conversation, for Glenaladale, who had been in conversation outside with Dr Cameron and Breackachie, now entered the Cage, and his coming aroused Lochiel. Meanwhile Cluny's gillies, who had learnt the news, were chattering in Gaelic at the tops of their voices, as they lit the fir candles and began to prepare a hurried breakfast.

Within an hour of Glenaladale's coming with the great news, the whole party had started on their journey to the coast. Because of the Prince's insistence that they went at a moderate pace, Dr Cameron had volunteered to go on ahead as fast as he could and inform the commander of the ship that they were on their way. A rough litter, made of a plaid fastened over stakes, was constructed for Lochiel, and this was borne by four of Cluny's gillies; and despite their burden, they trotted along so fast, even over rough ground, that the party had travelled some eight miles across the mountains before the first grey daylight overtook them. They had arrived at a place called Coir-a-Mhaighe, and here they rested all day, for being so large a party—besides the Prince, there were Cluny, Lochiel, Glenaladale, Breackachie, Allan Cameron, and four gillies—it was not considered safe to travel in daylight unless this became absolutely necessary. They refreshed themselves with the provisions which they had carried with them from the Cage, and, posting sentries, slept in the heather.

When night came on, they started out again, and by dawn had got over Glenroy. Again they rested till evening, undisturbed except for the peaceful sounds of men and women cutting their hay in the glen below them. On this last stage of the Prince's wanderings, the weather had turned fine and warm; the sun had lost its fierce heat, and the autumn cold was no more than an invigorating chill in the nights and early morning. It seemed that his beloved Highlands were determined to show themselves to Charles under their most kindly aspect, now that he was leaving them; the heather glowed in its last glory of purple, the bracken fronds were red and yellow, the clegs had lost their vicious bite, and the hills lay gentle and dreaming under the pale blue sky.

When they set out that night in bright moonshine, Lochiel told Charles that their way would take them near his house of Achnacarie, and although it had been burnt by the red soldiers and was only a ruin, he was very eager to show it to the Prince. Charles would much rather not have had to face the painful ordeal of seeing yet another great house which had become a blackened ruin, a reminder to him of the fate which had overtaken so many of his friends because of their loyalty to him, but he saw it would please Lochiel greatly if he agreed, so he said of course he would visit Achnacarie. As they went along, Cluny, who had been silent for some while, remarked that the problem which was worrying him was how they were to get over the river Lochy; they dared not go by the fords, for these would be guarded by the Militia, and it was much too deep and wide for them to swim it. "Besides," he added, with a meaning glance at Charles, "we have a wounded man in our midst."

"Then we must get a boat," said the Prince, shaking his head reprovingly at Cluny.

"I will send Allan Cameron on ahead to find one," said Lochiel, "for we are now come into my own country. The soldiers have plundered it so thoroughly that I doubt they will have left me one of my own boats, but it will be hard indeed if one of my clansmen has not contrived to hide some coble in which we may cross."

So Allan Cameron was sent on ahead, and when the rest of the party arrived at the river bank, they found him there in company with a relation of Lochiel's, Cameron of Cluns. He was a cheerful, vigorous man, with a beard stained brown with snuff, for he was much addicted to the habit of snuff-taking, for ever groping in his sporran for his snuff-mull, which was made of a piece of ram's horn, taking up a generous pinch, and then going into an absolute paroxysm of sneezing. When he was not sneezing he was laughing; everything seemed to amuse him, even his own destitute state, for like his

Chief, Lochiel, he had had his house burnt over him and had been forced to take to the heather.

" Ach, you may get over the Lochy very well whatever," said he, after the greetings were over, " for I have an old boat down-by, and it is the only one the enemy left of all your boats, Lochiel. Indeed, and it is a terrible old boat whatever, as full of holes as a riddle," and with that he went off into one of his fits of laughter.

When they came to the place where the boat was hidden, Charles saw that Cameron of Cluns had spoken no less than the truth. It was the most disreputable looking craft the Prince had ever seen, full of holes, with no pins for the oars, the bottom clogged with weed and barnacles, and the timber rotten. Even Lochiel and Cluny, who were used to sailing in all weathers in the frail Highland cobles, shook their heads at it, and told Cluns that certainly it would not be safe to cross the Lochy in it.

" It is as safe as a man-of-war," retorted Cluns, offended, " and to prove it, I will cross first, and if I drown, you may call me a liar." He roared with laughter, as though he had made an excellent joke. " There being so many of us," he added, wiping his eyes and reaching for his snuff-mull, " we shall be obliged to make more than one ferrying. But before we cross the river, I am at thinking we would all be the better for a dram. What says your Royal Highness ? Will you please to take a dram of brandy to warm you ? "

" I cannot think of anything I should like better,"

replied the Prince, " for I am mighty tired and chilled
with the night air. But how may we have brandy in
this desolate spot ? "

" Ach, I have six bottles of it, no less," answered
Cluns carelessly, " and I can promise your Royal Highness that it is good spirit, for I and some of my friends
were after making a raid upon a camp of the red soldiers
some weeks since, and from the officer's tent we took
this brandy as our spoil, it being all laid up in a case,
and designed, I believe, as a present for some great
personage. Indeed and surprise would not be on me if
I heard that this same brandy was bought for Butcher
Cumberland himself."

Cluns' story, and the triumphant way in which he told
it, made them all laugh, as, sitting down in the heather
on the river bank, they uncorked one of the bottles and
passed it round. The Prince accepted a pinch from
Cluns' snuff-mull, and as he did so, he noticed that the
mull had two little silver hands clasped round the ram's
horn, holding the motto *Rob Gib*.

" What does it mean, *Rob Gib* ? " he asked.

" Ach," replied Cluns, " we have a saying up here,
Rob Gib's Contract, which signifies stark love and friendship; knowledge is not at me how the term came to be
used, for it is as old as the mountains." He glanced at
the Prince, and this time he did not laugh. " When the
time comes for me to take farewell of your Royal Highness," said he, " I shall be asking you to accept this
snuff-mull as a gift, that when you make use of it in

France you may be reminded that across the sea there is a people whose stark love and friendship for you will have no ending."

When they had each had a dram or two of brandy, Cluns directed the gillies to push the old boat out into the water, and, taking Glenaladale and Breackachie with him, set out on the first ferrying, the others watching anxiously from the bank. The boat settled so low in the water that Charles feared at any moment to see her sink; when the treacherous currents caught her, she seemed as helpless as a person who cannot swim, and every eddy had her at its mercy. But after a very slow and hazardous voyage, she arrived safely at the other side, Cluns leaping ashore and waving his arms in triumph and encouragement, as he sent the gillies to take her back again. Now it was the Prince's turn to be ferried over, for Cluny, Lochiel, and Allan Cameron insisted on waiting until he was safe before the boat ventured on her third and last trip. By the time Charles had joined Cluns on the opposite bank, there was so much water in the boat that she would hardly move.

However, after baling her out, Cluns sent her back to fetch the remainder of the party, earnestly instructing the gillies not to forget to bring the rest of the brandy which he had left on the other side. Watching anxiously, the Prince saw the boat reach her destination, and the gillies clamber out of her to lift Lochiel on his litter into the crazy craft. It was a difficult business, and seemed to cause a great commotion; when at last the wounded man, with Cluny and Allan Cameron, was safely on board, the boat had settled so low in the water that from the opposite bank it looked as if her passengers were sitting in the river itself. Charles, frantic with anxiety for Lochiel, could scarcely bear to watch her slow progress, and his distress was increased by observing the behaviour of the gillies who had the task of rowing. For halfway across, they suddenly burst into song; it seemed a most unfitting thing to do in this hazardous situation, and sounded deafening in the silence of the night. Besides this, they wagged their heads about, dug at the water with their oars, and laughed and shouted as though they had gone mad. It was plain to the on-lookers on the bank that Cluny and Lochiel were trying to quiet them, but it was all to no purpose, for they behaved more like lunatics than ever.

" What in heaven's name is the matter with them ? " Charles cried to Cluns.

" They have the drink in them," replied Cluns, dancing up and down with laughter. " Ach, it is plain they have got at my brandy, a mischief be in their sides ! Look at that now, how they behave as if they had been taken out of themselves altogether. There will be some aching heads in the morning, I promise you."

Charles was less concerned about aching heads than Lochiel's safety, and as the boat approached the bank, he waded out into the water, anxious only to pull her and her precious cargo to land. Cluns assisted him and it was as well that he did, for just as she came into shallow water, the boat gave a last gurgle and then sank like a log. The Prince was relieved to find that Lochiel was no worse for the perilous voyage; indeed he was laughing almost as heartily as Cluns.

" The bottles of brandy were broken in the business of getting me on board," he explained to the Prince, " and the spirit mingling with the water we shipped, the gillies drank it up in the baling-can as though it had been punch, and nothing we could say would prevent them."

The Prince, observing the unsteady steps and stupid smiles of the gillies, shared his friend's amusement; but Cluny, whose clansmen they were, was in a frenzy of rage. Snatching up a stick from the bank, he laid about them, at the same time storming at them in a spate of Gaelic, even going so far as to draw his dirk and threaten them with instant death for their misbehaviour. His anger had the effect of sobering them completely, and when the party started to walk towards Achnacarie, they huddled together in the rear with the air of newly caned schoolboys.

It was early morning when the party came in sight of Achnacarie, and a melancholy sight it was, with its blackened stone and its charred timbers and its gardens trampled and defaced. Yet Lochiel, who seemed to feel pride rather than grief for his ruined home, persuaded Charles to make a tour of it, describing the escape of his wife and family, pointing out the thoroughness with which the red soldiers had plundered Achnacarie before putting it to the flames, of how they had stripped even the slates from the roof, the wainscot from the walls, and had chipped the coat-of-arms from over the door so that nothing remained to bear witness to its ownership. Instead of a house, he said, they had left him a monument to his loyalty, and the proud story to hand down to his children's children of how the Chief of the Camerons had lost all for his rightful King.

Afterwards he led the party to a hunting-lodge he had in the woods; here he had kept a store of oatmeal hidden for himself or such of his relations who might have occasion to conceal themselves from the soldiers. This oatmeal, with some beef which Allan Cameron obtained from some of his Chief's tenants, was destined to comprise all the food the party would have to sustain them until they reached Lochnanuagh and the French privateer.

They stayed in the hunting-lodge till it grew dark again, and then set off to walk through yet another night. All of them had fallen rather silent, as is the way with friends who know that, after a long time in each other's company, the hour of parting draws near. For though Lochiel and Glenaladale had agreed to embark with the Prince, Charles had not been able to persuade Cluny, Breackachie, or Cameron of Cluns to do so. Cluny was going back to his Cage, for, he said, his clansmen needed him, and also, being an old man, he could not endure the thought of dying in a foreign country. Indeed, Charles could hardly find it in his heart to ask any of these people to share the bitterness of exile, for from his long stay with them he had learnt how desperately dear to them was their native soil. Though their homes might be burnt and their clans scattered, though they themselves were in hourly peril of being captured and put to death, still they clung to the soil they knew, and preferred to roam their own mountains like the wild deer rather than live in comfort in an alien land.

By morning the wanderers had reached Camgharaiddh in the head of Loch Arkaig, and were nearly at the end of their journey. It had been plain to Charles for some time that Lochiel's wounds had been making the journey more and more painful to him, and so the Prince feigned an increase of his own sickness in order to insist that they stayed here, not only for the day but for the night as well. It was folly, he knew, to delay so long, for the gillies reported that some parties of the Militia were in the neighbourhood, and besides, the commander of the French ship might give them up for lost and sail away. But Charles was still determined to get Lochiel safely to their destination, and remained deaf to all Cluny's whispered remonstrances.

On the next afternoon, which was that of September 18th, they started in broad daylight for Boradale and the coast, having but a few miles to travel. Lochiel had never made one complaint, but his white face, drawn and sweaty with pain as he was jolted over the rough ground, was eloquent enough of his sufferings, and so it was not until the first light of dawn that they saw below them the loch which was their goal, and riding in it two strange ships. There were no flags at the mast-heads, no marks upon the vessels to show who they were, but this in itself informed the weary fugitives that here were the privateers who waited for them. The sight so mingled joy and grief in the breasts of the wanderers, that Cluns' laughter sounded hysterical, and the rest of them were stricken dumb.

A look-out on board one of the ships perceived the party through his spy-glass while they were still climbing down towards the loch, so that when they came to the shore they found a row-boat waiting to convey the Prince to the *Bellona*. Before he stepped into it, he turned to his companions and said that his resolve was not to allow Colonel Warren to weigh anchor until the following evening, so that such of his friends, whether gentleman or humble clansman, who got word of the presence of the ships, might have time to come to Lochnanuagh and share in his escape. Even Cluny knew him well enough by now not to attempt to argue with him, though they all knew it was madness to put off the hour of his going, lest others besides fugitives became aware that there were French ships in the loch.

All the little company which had escorted Charles from the Cage went on board the *Bellona* with him, those who were staying in Scotland wishing to remain with him until the last moment. His welcome to the ship was exultant, Colonel Warren telling him that by this time his royal father and everyone in France had despaired of ever seeing him again. The Colonel and his crew of volunteers exclaimed in horror at the Prince's ragged dress and insisted on his changing it at once for fair white linen, a good cloth coat and breeches, and a white peri-wig, but Charles refused. Laying one hand on Lochiel's shoulder and the other on that of Cluny, he smiled round upon the little band of comrades who had brought him safely, through so many dangers, to the ship, as he said in a voice which was a little shaky from emotion :

" All the velvet and the gold-lace and the jewels in the world will never be so much to my liking as this ragged old tartan plaid. With the help of God, I hope to wear it yet in the streets of London. And when that good day comes, my friends, you shall visit me at my father's palace, and we'll take a hearty dram of brandy, and remember how bravely we fared at Cluny's Cage."

" Well, look at that now ! " said Cluns, with a laugh which sounded suspiciously like a sob. " Your Royal Highness will be great and powerful then, and will not like to remember all the hardships and perils you suffered when you skulked in the heather of the Highland hills."

" We are to dine presently," replied the Prince, " on food such as we have not tasted for many months, seated at a finely laid table, with silver and linen and fair china. But for my part, this dinner will not taste as good to me as the deer-meat and the bannocks I have shared so often with my friends on some deserted island or in a herdsman's bothie with a leaky roof. For it is love and loyalty and comradeship which gives relish to a feast. My sorrow is that I must part from you now and from the land which I have grown to love so well, leaving you ruined, and having no reward to bestow upon you for your services."

Nobody spoke for a moment. Then Cluny seized the snuff-mull belonging to Cameron of Cluns, took a mighty pinch which made him almost explode with sneezing, and, when he had recovered himself, said stoutly :

" As for reward, you have seen, Mr Thomson, how little this thing called money means to my race, seeing that there has been no less than thirty thousand pounds lying ready to the hand of any poor man, ignorant and starving, who would have betrayed you. Many a shepherd and herdsman, many a beggar and outlaw, has known these past six months how to earn that reward, but, God be thanked, not one has stooped to such a crime. And now we have the reward which we prize above all things, which is the knowledge of your being delivered from the enemy who thirsted after your blood. But by the hand of my ancestors, Mr Thomson," added Cluny, becoming his haughty little self again as he remembered an old grievance, " it is the providence of God alone which has worked this miracle, for the enemy was less to be feared than your own obstinacy in dallying so long upon your journey, and you will pardon me if I say so plainly to your face."

Charles laughed at this rebuke, but he was still as obstinate as ever in his care for his friends, and all that day, the following night, and the next day again, he refused to let the commander of the privateer weigh anchor, until as many fugitives as possible had come on board. They came singly or in twos and threes, desperate, starving, ragged men, who had been skulking in the heather ever since Culloden and had never thought to escape. At last, when, late on Saturday, September 20th, the *Bellona* and her sister-ship hoisted sail, the Prince had the satisfaction of knowing that the hazardous delay on which he had insisted had enabled more than a hundred of his faithful Highlanders to share in his escape to France.

The story of his wanderings was over, and he was safe. But that story would live for ever in the memories of those who had taken part in it, and who had been the means of bringing about the most miraculous deliverance that ever happened in real life. And whatever became of Prince Charles Edward Stuart in the future, the remembrance of his gallantry in danger, his endurance of hardship, his cheerfulness in discomfort, and his eternal thoughtfulness for others, would ensure that to those who knew and loved him he would ever remain, King of the Highland hearts, Bonnie Prince Charlie.